Non-Sync, Tabs & Cream Soda

A Socko Performance of Tragedy, Romance, Ambition & Triumph

by: Philip C. Rosen

Published by:

38CENTIGRADE

Find out more about products by 38 Centigrade at:

www.38centigrade.com

Editor: G.K.F. Littardi

Interior Design: G.K.F. Littardi

Production: G.K.F. Littardi

Cover Design and Production: G.K.F. Littardi

Proof-reading: Judith H. Littardi

Should you discover and wish to report any errors, please send a note to **errata@38centigrade.com**

Credits

My thanks must go to the following people, as without them my book would not be in front of you as it is now:

To my wife Sheila Rosen:
The best woman in the whole world. Thank you love for your secretarial skills, patience in typing up the original manuscript and for correcting many of the initial grammatical goofs!

To my daughter Judith Littardi:
Tireless proof-reader of the edited manuscript. A European language speaker and translation specialist, Judith works freelance as a credit manager for European markets, European translator and is mother to Massimo Littardi.

To my son-in-law Karl Littardi:
For his phenomenal patience, fastidious editing, huge enthusiasm, creative direction and expert technical knowledge. The brains behind www.38centigrade.com Karl is a successful freelance manuscript editor, publishing agent, design consultant and software engineer.

Lastly, I'd just like to say that for the pioneering work of Karl and others like him, in this relatively new field of publishing, I have admiration; admixed with some degree of awe at what is now possible (many like me will have once found all this quite impossible to imagine).

Contents

Foreword

From the Editor and Publishing Agent, Karl Littardi (year: 2011).

First, I wish to thank you, the reader, for buying this book. I hope you enjoy reading it as much as Phil and I have enjoyed preparing it for you.

A recurring historical cliche, I know, but these really are extraordinary times. Without doubt, today's youngsters take for granted so much - largely that which their elders are so proud to have been early adopters. Where oldies have the benefit of hindsight for comparison, young 'uns are less able to appreciate the differential. Their day inevitably comes, and I hope they enjoy that experience as much as I have in my lifetime.

While I am Phil's editor and publishing agent, I am also especially fortunate to be his son-in-law; having married his truly extraordinary daughter. Proud to have grown up during a veritable digital revolution, I had the foresight myself to embrace the computing industry. It was a time of early adopters and quite the fledgling sport for bright youngsters. Just as Phil's inventions have changed the very fabric of how we live (reliability and safety provided by timeless industrial electrical engineering), so it is that digital electronics leads us to a world much more convenient and accessible to so many.

'The People' are now quite able to achieve their dreams, with much less red tape and such standing in the way. Those of you reading this text on an electronic reading device, take a moment to imagine how that would be possible without a reliable national electrical network. How would you charge the batteries in your device ... or would you have the device at all?

As a younger man, Phil attempted to publish this story, based on his own life; but his manuscript was rejected by those publishers so characteristically officious at the time. The belligerent Phil wouldn't let go, however; and I think you will agree, it's a shame that the story was not available before.

You have in front of you now a rare, first-hand account of life during 1940s Britain, through the eyes of a genuine citizen of Liverpool, England (the one in the UK that is).

The setting: a time when the closest thing to the widespread communications we know today, was a one-way communication experience with the public via wooden-cased wireless radio sets ("This is the BBC World Service ..."). Back then, the world was simpler and less accessible to the common man; people in general were much less spoiled than appears to be the case today.

It is my great pleasure to present to you Phil's book. Personally, I look forward to the future with great anticipation ... to all forthcoming, seemingly miraculous technologies and markets we shall witness in our lifetimes.

As Phil would say: "**Read and Enjoy!**"

Introduction

This is an autobiographical account of my career as a Jewish cinema projectionist, way back in the late 1940s. In those distant, pre-TV times, the cinema was enormously popular. Most families went at least once or twice a week, enduring the cigarette smoke of the local flea pit. Watching the films was a well-established form of escapement; an antidote, no less, to the grim austerity of the post-war years. My involvement during the humble end of the cinema industry began in 1948, soon after leaving school, and continued for nearly seven years.

From the flea-pit projectionist to my first steps into professional electrical engineering, I was a determined individual; determined to better myself and, importantly, to do it with something I loved being involved in - electrical engineering. Learning as a teenager to repair old wireless radio sets, which were donated to me by my barber, I found my calling.

I went on to carve a fabulous career as a world-class, pioneering engineer. But, it was no walk in the park ... it was, however, quite a fun ride in parts and I have never looked back!

I hope you enjoy reading my story as much as I enjoyed living it, writing about it and going through the process of putting it into your hands.

Thankyou,

Phil Rosen

By the way, all the incidents and characters portrayed are entirely factual, only the names of the dramatis personae have been changed as a courtesy to those involved.

Prologue

A bright, sunny spring morning. The year, 1948. Now less than three years since the war ended, no more are there air raid sirens, blackouts or bombs ... but times are still hard. Food, clothes and almost everything else is in short supply, as it's still all rationed. The standard of living, far lower than today, means very few can afford a car, or even a fridge or telephone. Still, we HAD beaten the Germans and the Japs. Life was safe once again, and that was by far the most important thing.

I was at this time, when this story kicks off, a gangling teenager of sixteen. I had left school a few weeks earlier and was on my way to work, at my first job ... as a grocer's boy. I didn't like the job, but it was all I could get. I hated the smell of the cheese and bacon, and all the other grocery pongs. However, although I didn't know it, this would be my last day behind the counter. I was, as we shall see, destined to begin my career in show business ... sort of!

My home town of Wallasey was a kind of huge suburb of Liverpool, but on the other side of the River Mersey. I lived with my mum and dad, at one end of the town, and had a mile or so to walk each day to the grocery store in the shopping centre. On the way I would pass our little synagogue; where, very occasionally, my dad would persuade me to attend service. Given Dad was quite religious, I was a sad disappointment to him when it came to the Jewish faith.

Roads were very quiet in those days. Really hardly any traffic around compared to the endless stream of cars, trucks and the solid jams common today ... It was quite peaceful walking to work along the Liscard Road ...

Tall, with trousers too short, I wore the regulation baggy flannel trousers with turn-ups. Looking down anxiously to see if the hole in my sock was showing, my shirt had a separate stiff collar fastened by a brass stud (which kept working loose and the damned ends kept springing out). I had got into the habit of automatically fiddling with the thing whenever someone came up to me. Also, regulation sleeveless woollen pullover and long gabardine raincoat.

Like almost all men in those days, I still wore some kind of hat. Men wore bowler hats or trilbies, whereas working-class teenagers like me wore a flat cap. There was a breeze that morning; so whenever I wasn't checking my socks or my shirt stud, I hung on to my peaked cap to stop the thing blowing off down the road.

In an effort to stop fidgeting, I stuck my hands firmly in my pockets and whistled one of the latest hit songs on the radio at the time. In those almost unbelievably primitive times, before mobile phones or MP3 players, we had to make do with our own thoughts and make our own music as we walked along. I must admit that I feel it was also perhaps a friendlier age than today.

"'Ello, lad. Yawright?"

As I looked up I found myself waving to a neighbour: Mrs. Flanagan, looming towards me with her laden shopping basket. She was a stout lady and wore a heavy shapeless coat against the chill breeze.

She was a bit careless as to dress - I couldn't help but notice her stockings were wrinkled about her ankles (Nora Batty!), and She wore a headscarf tightly knotted under her chin.

"On your own then Young Phil? No Judy yet?"

I shook my head shyly and edged away to avoid a delay over those lengthy bulletins on her lumbago. Daft old bat! Even if I had a 'Judy' I wouldn't be seeing her at 08.30 on a Monday morning! Incidentally, taking a girl out in those days was a much more circumspect business. Things seldom went much further than a kiss, and maybe even a cuddle. Strange times!

Quickening my pace, not wanting to be late, I broke into a rendition of the marching tune on the Saturday night radio show (ta rum te ta, ta rum te ta, ..., etc). We listened to the radio at home most evenings, as television was still just over the horizon. What we DID have, as our main source of entertainment, was the local cinema. This was, in the 1940s, an enormously popular evening out.

It was relatively inexpensive, with most families going at least once or twice a week. However, one had to brave the cigarette smoke and watch black and white films (this as a kind of escape from all the grim austerity of the post war years).

My own involvement with the cinema began on the day this story opens, continuing for over six years until I was able to enter into my true vocation as an electrical engineer.

To avoid jumping the gun any further, for the moment, I have just arrived rather dusty and breathless at the door of Maypole Grocery Stores Ltd.

Mrs. Marshall the manageress ushers me inside all grim-faced ... oh, what now?

Reel One

Monday and Tuesday this week:

"Old Mother Riley in Paris"

also

"Rock River Renegades"

"Is it because of the coupons?" I asked.

Mr. Potters nodded grimly, his expression one of severe disapproval. We faced each other across the little office desk: Mr. Potters, the staff superintendent of Maypole Grocery stores (Ltd), a silver-haired, fussily efficient little man and myself, at that time, a shambling, acne-infested youth of sixteen-years.

"But why?" I burst out, full of injured innocence. "The war's been over for more than three years now. Food isn't that short. Why on earth should we have to bother ... snipping thousands of tiny bits of paper out of people's ration books and then count them up and then sort them out and then ..."

Mr. Potters raised a magisterial hand "I am not really concerned with your political opinions, young man.

I am much more concerned with the idea that you might well have landed us all behind bars by now."
He shuddered and bent to peer shortsightedly at some notes on his desk.

"Mrs. Marshall (the shop manageress) says," he intoned severely "that on several occasions recently, she caught you red-handed selling groceries without asking the customers for their ration books. She has particularly noticed it with packets of strawberry table jelly. Young man, explain yourself!"

I flinched before Mr. Potters's outraged glare, answering with some hesitation.
"Er, well ... you see sir, jellies was one of the few things Mrs. Marshall trusted me to sell on my own. Exactly sixpence a packet you see, so I wasn't likely to get the change muddled up so easy. Rinso and baked beans were also dead easy to work out, but I had terrible problems with the cheese. All them ounces, and pennies and ha'pennies, and then working out the change. Mrs. Marshall said ..."

"That will do, that will do." Mr. Potters cut in and, after regaining his self control: "May one ask, Philip, how you passed your time in-between waiting for the great moment when a customer came in wanting a packet of jelly, a tin of baked beans and some Rinso?"

To which I replied, "Well I mostly polished the brass weights on the scales with Brasso, and sieved out the mouse droppings from the lentils and pearl barley, and made the others their cups of tea of course!"

Mr. Potters peered at his notes again ... "And then Philip, there was the question of your delivery methods. You were observed actually rolling one of our big round cheeses along the pavement to our Wallasey Village branch."

"Well you see sir, I can't ride a bike and the cheese was too heavy to carry, so I ..." I said, in a feeble attempt to counter his interrogation.

To my surprise, Mr. Potters seemed to suddenly regain some of his good humour. He was actually quite cheerful when, gathering together some papers on his desk, he said:

"Well Philip, to be frank, we really don't seem quite suited to each other do we? Of course we in Maypole Stores wish you every success in your future career, whatever that may be. I think you will find these documents are complete. I have included a week's salary in lieu of notice, so you can go as soon as you like."

He handed me my cards, shook hands and gave what he no doubt intended as a friendly smile.

"It's rather busy in the shop just now. Shall I carry on helping out 'till we close?" I asked, in an attempt to be helpful to the last.

Mr. Potters' smile froze. "No, no!" he shouted with quite unnecessary violence. Then, with the calmness of despair ...

"Mrs. Marshall tells me the locals have passed the word around about you. Apparently they form queues where you are serving to get their ration-free goods. The other assistants are left twiddling their thumbs. We shall be ruined. Please, please, just go!"

I could take a hint and I went, promptly marching out of Maypole Grocery Stores ...

I had found the work to be dreadfully boring and, sadly, made no real attempt to understand the business. I just wasn't cut out to be a grocer's boy. Having left school only two months earlier, I had an undefined yearning to embark on some highly-technical career; one that would involve me in masses of wires, switches, glowing valves and flickering meters ... not unlike a mad professor in his laboratory, if you will.

"I should like to be a wireless repair man or an electrician." I announced at the Youth Employment Bureau, waving my School Leaving Certificate (my sole scholastic attainment) at an unimpressed Youth Employment Officer.

"With your complete lack of education? No chance sonny!" exclaimed the official firmly, as he deftly fished a little green card out of his file. "Take this along to Maypole Grocery Store. They want a grocer's boy. That's more your style."

I threaded my way among the bustling crowds of shoppers and set off for home - a young lad with a weighty problem on his mind. Now we weren't starving, but money was tight and my small, thirty-five shillings per-week, wage packet had been a useful addition to the family. Besides, self-respect made repugnant the idea of lounging around at home without any visible means of support. I had to get another job as quickly as possible. My fond hopes of becoming an electrical technician of some kind, were fading fast; and I was mentally reviewing and rejecting images of myself in a shoe shop, a gents' outfitters, a bakery, or perhaps even another grocery store (hell!).

I shuddered with a gloomy sigh, and continued on my way past Central Park. Its bright flower beds and, atop the town war memorial, a most attractive Britannia with great big stone tits seemed to watch as I continued on, passing the elegant red brick Victorian villas ... past Griffiths the undertakers, and on towards Seacombe. This, the older, shabbier part of town where we lived. I was still debating how to break the news at home. What would my dad say? What excuses would I make for being fired? ... and so on ...

I arrived opposite the Kings Picture House, stopping idly for a moment outside the little cinema, to see what was on that week.

'Paulette Goddard and Ray Milland in "Kitty" - a great romantic love story' read the little hoarding over the foyer. "Romance? Yuk!"

About to turn away in disgust, I noticed a small hand-written card, tucked into a corner of the notice board.

"Junior projectionist wanted. Apply within."

This sounded interesting. More than that, exciting even. I wanted to apply for the job right away; to be right there at the forefront of a desperate horde of job-hungry young men, who'd be bound to apply for such an attractive post.

As I looked around, the little cinema dozed peacefully in the afternoon sunshine. There wasn't anyone about. A rusty, black, folding metal grille across the tiny foyer, kept passing mongrels from piddling on the little flight of marble steps leading from the street up to a tiny pay box.

Rattling the bars, I called:

"Hello anyone there?" a couple of times ... but silence.

I stood there, in my frustration, grasping the iron bars like some megalithic tomb raider, trying to raise the spirits of ages past. Presently, one of those spirits could be heard somewhere ... pounding hollowly down some stone staircase within. Then, a little door next to the pay desk, about four feet high, flew open and disgorged a young giant. He had a shock of flaming-red hair and uncoiled himself from the inadequate doorway. Towering down from behind the bars, he told me severely that the matinee didn't start till Two O'Clock.

"No, no, I've come about the job!" I said diffidently, pointing at the card.

"Oh that's different ..." said the giant, grinning in a friendly manner, "... hop over the bars and I'll take you up to see the manager."

With some difficulty, I scaled the rusty bars, landing heavily beside the red-haired giant in the tiny foyer.

"I'm Dennis Mills, the chief projectionist," said the red-haired giant, with a finger-numbing handshake, "follow me."

With a wild yell of defiance, like the mad uncle in 'Arsenic and Old Lace,' Dennis flung open the little door, launching himself up the narrow shin-breaking, stone spiral staircase. A bit shaken, I stumbled up behind him as well as I could. Dennis' great bulk twisted into fantastic contortions, as as he charged up the staircase.

He stopped at a little door, which opened off the stairs about half way up. Flinging open the door, he announced "Mr. Clapshaw, the manager!" Dennis pounded off up the stairs and out of sight.

I stepped nervously inside to find myself in an office about the size of a large double-wardrobe. There was an elbow-deep pile of paperwork, flanked by a large drum of flea killer on one side; the other a sack of peas. Wedged into a corner, at a desk was Mr. Harold Clapshaw; manager of the Kings Picture House. I coughed, and was about to speak when he motioned me to be quiet. So, I just stood in the doorway, waiting until he had finished what he was doing.

A pale, thin man, Mr. Clapshaw was about twenty-five years old. He was, I suppose, quite handsome, with a mouthful of flashing white teeth, and jet black hair sleeked down with hair cream. He was dressed in the regulation cinema manager's uniform, comprising a slightly threadbare evening suit, and dress shirt with pearl studs. He was occupied in picking up peas one at a time from the sack next to him, dropping them into a large glass jar on his desk.

"1037, 1038, 1039, 1040, ..." he whispered to himself.

"Right, that will do ..." he said, finally screwing the lid on the jar. Flashing his teeth again, in a mechanical, patron-welcoming smile "... you've come about the job, I suppose? Well come in, sit down and tell me all about yourself."

Squeezing inside, I sat on the drum of flea killer. With no notion of interview techniques, I gave a frank account of my lack of education, being sacked from the grocery store and the domestic circumstances which made it imperative for me to find employment quickly.

Mr. Clapshaw smiled. Then, with finger tips pressed together in clerical fashion, spoke of his cinema, the enviable reputation of his staff ("one big happy family"), and of the incalculable risks to take in letting me loose among his dedicated, and highly-efficient workforce ... still, he would take that risk:

"Young men must be given the opportunity to advance themselves; and in the cinema industry, the opportunities for advancement are truly immense. You can have the job Philip." said Mr. Clapshaw with another beaming smile.

I was greatly relieved, but there were a few details I wanted clarified. Asking about the hours of duty, the kind of work I would be expected to do and ... pay, of course ... Mr. Clapshaw looked pained.

"At one time ..." pausing in a slightly offended tone "... trainee projectionists were looked upon as apprentices and they paid us for the privilege of being trained. However, you will be lucky enough to get an actual salary. We are prepared to offer you twenty-two shillings and sixpence per week." (This amounted to £1.12p per-week in today's money: 2010).

Mr. Clapshaw paused again, as if to allow the munificence of his offer to sink in. Now, I later learned that even an experienced "chief" was on only three-pounds per-week. So, although the offer was less than I had received as a grocers boy, perhaps it was not as outrageously low as it may have seemed at the time.

"As regards your job," Mr. Clapshaw continued "you will be employed as trainee projectionist; but you will also be expected to perform several other duties from time-to-time. Your hours will be ten in the morning until eleven in the evening, with some time off for dinner and tea. You will work six days a week, but ..." added Mr. Clapshaw "... you needn't come in Sunday mornings unless something special crops up."

I did a hurried calculation. "But Mr. Clapshaw, that must work out at over sixty-five hours a week!"

"That's true, the hours are rather short compared with the old days. Today you youngsters have an easy time of it in many ways. I'm not at all sure if it's a good thing all this leisure and pocket money!"

He seemed quite serious in what he was saying as he stood up and shook hands with me over the jar of peas on his desk. His smile, a little less mechanical and rather more friendly than before: "We'll see how you shape-up Philip. There may be some scope for a salary increase when you have proved you can do the job. Start Monday morning. Alright?"

I nodded, left Mr. Clapshaw gazing thoughtfully at his pea jar, and stumbled down the little staircase into the bright sunshine.

Continuing my interrupted walk homewards, I was now in a happier frame of mind. The job had its drawbacks for sure, but it was at least a job. I had at least snatched myself from the jaws of the dole queue, but wondered how Dad would take the news ...

"Nu?" said my father as we sat down to a late lunch. "How was it today?"

I waded stoically through the mound of potato cakes, which were held to be Dad's particular specialty, but to be more accurate, were one of the few things he had ever learned to cook at all.

"I got the sack!" I said "They told me I was no good at the job."

Dad was quite unconcerned at the news. " Well, these things happen. So now you'll take up the tailoring business like I've always wanted you to ..."

"No Dad NO!" I spluttered indignantly. "I've must have told you a hundred times. I'm very sorry, but I just can't follow in your footsteps. I could never take to cutting and sewing jackets and trousers, and putting the buttons on and all that. I want to do something in the electrical line, you know that."

"With no education?" Dad shook his head sadly. "Why you can't even do simple arithmetic let alone anything technical. Why break your head over things which are too complicated for you to understand? Now, a nice straightforward job in gents outfitting ..."

"I've already got a new job." I interrupted with some difficulty. I explained what sort of job it was, the hours, the pay and so on. His face, fell. We both knew what the matter was.

"What will your mother say?" he finally exploded in the greatest anxiety. "You know how upset she can get. Oy! I don't know how we are going to tell her, I really don't."

I sympathised with Dad. My Mother could be an extremely difficult person at times, and would work herself up into a fierce passion over quite trivial things. How she would react to my new job scarcely bore thinking about (with hindsight, she would have done well to have locked me in the coal cellar for a week until someone else got the job).

Next day was Saturday, and visiting day at Deva mental hospital, where Mum was being treated for one of her periodic bouts of persecution complex. Deva was out in the country far from the troublesome neighbours who were trying to poison or, electrocute her (we were never quite sure which).

Dad and I ambled across the dock estate, which divided our town from neighbouring Birkenhead and, having cleared the lines of rusty barges and tramp steamers, boarded the low-roofed green Crosville bus at Woodside Ferry. We left grimy smoke-laden Birkenhead behind and rattled through the leafy Wirral lanes. We got off at Deva hospital; a great sprawling barracks of a place, but set in pleasant parkland. The prevailing impression was one of endless tiled corridors and an countless locked, barred doors; like a sort of rural Strangeways prison. Patients met their visitors in a vast gloomy hall like a seedy run down cafe where, around scores of little tables, they chatted nervously over countless cups of WRVS tea.

Mum took the news of my dismissal from the grocers shop in a calm, practical manner. These things happened and I was sure to get another job soon. Then we told her about my new job as a cinema projectionist and, with good reason, awaited her reaction nervously.

"Oh no" she wailed "not in a cinema, not my little boy in one of those dreadful places. You must stop him Avrom. You must go and tell the manager he is too young. It would be a crime ..."

It turned out she had little concern about the long hours, the bad working conditions or the pitiful salary. Her worry, as it turned out, was of a completely unexpected nature.

"Those usherettes!" she almost shrieked "Those awful loose women. They'll take away his innocence; perhaps even trap him into some dreadful marriage. He is not to go there!"

Going home afterwards on the bouncing, rattling top deck of the Crosville bus, I pondered her words, wondering what she could possibly have meant. Could it be that working in a cinema might have some hitherto unexpected attractions for a young lad like me after all?

Asking Dad what he thought: "I don't know what she meant. You know she is a bit meshuggah just now." he said gruffly, burying his nose in the 'Jewish Times.'

I had a suspicion he was laughing but couldn't be quite sure.

Reel Two

Wednesday and Thursday this week:

"Tahiti Nights"

also

"Prison Breakers"

Wallasey, where I lived, was a medium-sized town facing the great port of Liverpool across the Mersey. It was a dormitory suburb where, each morning, the town would empty itself out into crowded ferry boats and carry the workers across the river to the tramcars, which clanked and rumbled them on their way to the factories and offices where they spent their day. At around five O'Clock in the evening, the whole process would be repeated in reverse. The kettles and frying pans would sizzle, the evening meal 'put away' and then, perhaps two- or three-times-a-week, it was off to the pictures. It was cheap entertainment. Even a good seat in the balcony might cost no more than one shilling (10p). So, not really a big drain on the housekeeping. In any case, in those dark days before the advent of TV and Video, it was the only form of family entertainment on offer.

At that time there were no less than thirteen cinemas in the town. About one cinema seat for every ten inhabitants. The most luxurious was the twelve-hundred seat 'Gaumont' in Egremont, near the river. With its profusion of art-deco decoration; including two large bas-relief carvings of nude female camera operators over the portico, and deep purple carpeting; it exuded an air of subdued grandeur.

Opposite, perched precariously almost on the river bank, was the long, narrow 'Royal' cinema. There, one gazed down at the distant silver screen from the back stalls as though through a railway tunnel complete with smoke.

At the nearby Liscard shopping centre were two more cinemas: the huge barn-like 'Capitol' and its rather sleazy threadbare neighbour the 'Liscard Palace.' In Poulton, with its stucco urns, the 'Queens': strings of vine leaves, polished brass-work and velvet curtains - it harked back to the very earliest days of the cinema, in Edwardian times. In Wallasey Village, the 'Coliseum', with its domes and turrets; it had recently been destroyed by fire, but was being rebuilt as a modern cinema, appropriately named the 'Phoenix.' Out in the backwoods, the mock-tudor beams of the 'Moreton Picture House' catered for those living on the edge of town.

At the New Brighton, day-trippers end of town, there was the large 'Winter Gardens.' It was well-equipped for doubling up as a theatre for live shows during the season, and not without a fine cinema organ too. Nestling amid the fish and chip shops and amusement arcades of nearby Victoria Road, was the weather-beaten facade of the 'Trocadero', which filled up rapidly with day-trippers whenever the weather turned suddenly nasty. The snug little 'Court' cinema, was just along the road.

Down by Seacombe ferry, the 'Marina' cinema haughtily turned its back on the tugs and ferries fussing up and down the river just behind it; not always succeeding in shutting out the sound of their hooters from the auditorium.

Starring gloomily at the cabbages in the grocer's shop opposite, in Seacombe itself (around the corner from our home) the grandly stuccoed 'Henry Irving' theatre; with its bust of the great Victorian actor high on its facade. Following the theatre's illustrious past, it was now, as its neon lights proclaimed, the 'Embassy Cinema'.

Last, and certainly the least, of all this varied collection, was the 'King's Picture House', which the fates had ordained as my shrine of initiation into the mysteries of show business!

The 'King's Picture House' was almost unbelievably small, a tiny matchbox-shaped building squeezed into a row of grubby little shops. It had once been the local jail and police court; at least until the town, and hence its population of wrongdoers, outgrew its very limited resources. It was now the smallest, least pretentious, and financially most precarious cinema on Merseyside. As if to emphasise its modesty, the facade was actually painted a dingy black throughout.

The foyer was so small that the doorman could practically seal it off by standing on the little flight of marble steps, flinging his arms out on either side. They ran no less than five separate programmes each week; mostly old, second-rate films, that the major cinemas had shown years before. The 'King's' fought a continuous, gallant battle for survival against its many, more glamorous competitors.

Hence salaries were as low and hours as long as the owners could screw out of the long-suffering, but loyal staff. I was the latest addition to this staff and was evidently to be screwed just as hard as any other.

At ten O'Clock, Monday morning, I reported for work. To my relief there was a gap in the iron gates across the foyer, allowing me to squeeze through instead of having to clamber over. Stumbling up the spiral staircase, I tapped on Mr. Clapshaw's door to find him, at this early hour, already immaculate in his snow-white shirt and dress suit. He was busy filling a large spray, about the size of of an elephant gun, from a drum of foul-smelling liquid labelled 'perfumed insecticide - trade use only'.

"Good morning, Philip" he said pleasantly, squirting the flea killer in an experimental manner up at the office ceiling. The tiny room stank abominably of the scented liquid, but Mr. Clapshaw seemed quite undaunted. He then handed me a large glass jar full of peas, which he had no doubt filled pea-by-pea from the open sack lying beside it ...

"Just take this down to the pay box. Then you can report to Dennis in the projection room."

As I staggered down the stairs clutching the pea jar, I wondered for the umpteenth time what part the peas played in the running of the cinema. Were they sold as a delicacy along with the choc-ices? Perhaps they were fired by the doorkeeper using a pea shooter, to quell noisy elements in the audience! They were in such short supply, that they had to be counted out one-by-one? I dumped the heavy jar down on the pay desk, giving the thing up as a mystery.

Going back upstairs, I passed Mr. Clapshaw's open door and saw him, still in evening dress, mixing what looked like a bucket of whitewash and humming: "There'll always be an England" the whole while. Further up the spiral stairs, a second little door opened off. Labelled "staff room", it was ajar. Inside a seemingly impossibly tiny-little room, were two upright chairs, a small table and, completely filling the rest of the space, two good-humoured Charladies supping tea.

"'Ello lad. Wanna cuppa?" they called in friendly fashion. Shaking my head I grinned shyly, carrying on to the very top of the stairs; where a massive steel door with 'no smoking' stenciled on it barred the way.

Pushing the door open, I was at once greeted by the pungent, vinegary smell which was to be my constant companion for the next seven years; clinging to my clothes and hair, and following me around like a malodorous shadow. The room was, I learned, the 'Rewind Room.' It was windowless and dimly lit, with bare brick walls and a stone floor. Two large fire extinguishers were placed within easy reach and, on the wall above, a handwritten notice in beautiful copper-plate script read:

"In case of fire - shut the door and run like bloody hell."

Along one wall was a zinc-topped bench bearing the re-winding machines. These were used to assemble each film programme while checking and rewinding films after each showing. Piled on the bench in some confusion, were the spools and odd lengths of film; which would presumably be joined together to form that night's programme.
Bottles of partly-used film cement stood around, accounting for the pungent reek which formed my first impression. I looked with some curiosity at the odd bits and pieces of film, which littered the rewind bench - 'coming shortly', 'next week only', 'eat Scraggs tripe' (it's true!),'God save the King'... it looked hopelessly complicated and, with a sinking feeling in my stomach, I thought of all the chaos that would ensue should one happen to muddle them, out of order.

I slid open a second, heavy steel door to find myself in the projection room proper. It was larger than the first, but more dimly lit, brick-walled and stone-floored. Neat and orderly, to me it was as impressive as a ship's engine room. In the centre the two cinema projectors grimly stood side-by-side, like a pair of cowled, complicated martian warriors. Alongside them, like some gawky-legged offspring, the little slide projector nestled in their shadow. The walls were lined from floor-to-ceiling with a most satisfying array of gleaming dials, knobs, levers, cables, switches and mysterious bits of apparatus.

"Morning Phil - you're late!"

Dennis appeared from behind the far projector, wielding an oil can and an oily rag.

"Sorry," I said, "but Mr. Clapshaw sent me on a message first."

Dennis grinned: "Only joking. You mustn't take me too seriously."

Rolling up his sleeves purposefully, he continued ...

"Well now you've arrived we must get to work. We've got a lot of jobs to get through, what with Wally being off."

"Who's Wally?" I asked, hanging up my frayed sports jacket.

"Wally is the second Op. You'll meet him tomorrow."

"Pardon? What's a second Op?"

Dennis rubbed his ear with the spout of the oil can, and replied with forced calmness:

"I can see before we start I'll have to teach you some of our lingo. For a start, we're not projectionists, we're "Operators" see? I'm the chief Op. Wally is second Op. and you'll be third Op. If and when you learn your job that is. This room is the 'Operating Box'. These projectors here are called the 'mechs'. Those windows looking into the auditorium are called 'ports'. These here ..."

He named half a dozen more items, patting each bit of equipment and giving it's colloquial title in rapid succession.

"... at any rate ..."

Breaking in, I pointed to the only bit of equipment I could clearly recognise:

"That's the gramophone, where you play the records in the interval. I can see that."

"Gramophone! We don't call it a Gramophone!" said Dennis scornfully. "That's the 'non-sync' that is ... it's called the 'non-sync'" said Dennis, hurriedly anticipating my next question, "because, in the old days before sound tracks were invented, the sound for the films was carried on huge gramophone records. These were played on a gramophone turntable attached to each projector. They were synchronised to run at exactly the same speed as the film, so the sound and the actions on the film wouldn't get out of step. So, the separate gramophone used for playing ordinary musical records during the interval, was called the 'non-synchronised turntable', or just 'non-sync' for short."

"And what about the sound tracks they use nowadays? How do they work?" I asked.

"Look" said Dennis, not unkindly, "there's a hell of a lot of work to be got through before the show starts, so no more questions for now. In big cinemas like the Odeon in Liverpool, they have four or five operators - to do the same work as we do with only two, and an apprentice like yourself. So we have to work twice as bloody hard to get it all done; especially when one of us (like today) has the day off. You'll just have to learn things as you go along."

Passing me the oil can and oily rag: "You just oil the projectors - that has to be done every day - and I'll go next door and get the films made up ready for the matinee. Call out when you're ready for the next job."

I found that each projector was covered in a rash of little capped oil receptacles, and each had to have its regulation two squirts of oil each day; this to prevent the machine from seizing up and becoming several thousand pounds-worth of scrap metal.

After working for a while in the operating box, I sensed that this room, like the other parts of the building, had its own particular aroma. It was a dry, dusty smell as of cinders and ashes and made your nose and throat tickle until you got used to it.

"Ready for your next job?" shouted Dennis, as he appeared from the rewind room with swathes of loose film, draped like a cobra around his shoulders. I nodded and, putting down the oil can, received a small brush and dust pan, and instructions on cleaning out the arc lamps (another daily chore it seemed).

The projector arc lamps produced the intense white light required to project the tiny image, within the film, onto the large, distant screen. This light was generated by an electric arc, which fizzled and spluttered between the tips of a pair of carbon rods (about the size of pencils) inside the lamp house. The rods burned away, while emitting clouds of white ash (the smell I had noticed earlier); some of which went up the chimney which sat over each projector.

One hoped that only a small proportion went into the lungs of the operators close by. The remainder clung in a film all over the machinery inside the lamp house. It was this which had to be chipped-, brushed- and dusted-away by the apprentice operator before each performance.

While Dennis worked away in the rewind room, preparing the matinee programme, I swept the stone floor, dusted and polished all the equipment, and fetched and carried reels and cases of film for Dennis. I was also occasionally called away by Mr. Clapshaw to help with such daily chores as whitewashing the treads of all the steps (so that patrons did not trip over in the dark), spraying the seats with flea killer, and making sure all the usherettes' ice-cream trays lit up properly.

"Is that the lot? Can I go now Dennis?" I panted, long after the time for my official lunch break had passed.

"Just one more job, then you can bugger off." answered Dennis with a grin. "Through that door is the outside emergency exit staircase, down to the street. All the dogs and cats in the neighbourhood use it as their favourite bog. We have to sweep away all the sh*te, every few days to make sure that if there's a fire and we have to make a run for it, we don't go sliding on our arses clear down to the bottom."

Thrusting a broom and shovel into my hand ... "Here you are then. Get going and be sure to get back from lunch by a-quarter-to-two."

Back home ...

"Nu?" said my father, as we sat over a hurried lunch.

"They haven't sacked you yet?"

"No" I answered shortly.

I loathed semolina pudding, but it happened to be one of the few dishes my dad specialised in. I stirred the gluey mess round in distaste.

"At least the work is interesting I suppose?" persisted my Father.

"Well, so far I've oiled the projectors, swept the floor, dusted and polished, killed bugs, white-washed steps, fetched and carried 'till my arms were dropping off, and finished by sweeping all the dog poo off the outside stairs." I answered.

"You expect your manager Mr. Clapshaw should do it? Someone has to do all these jobs and you're the new boy. Just have patience."

My father's logic was, as always, first class. I only wished I could have said the same about his semolina pudding.

Reel Three

Friday and Saturday this week:

"The Eagles Blood"

also

"Hills of Old Wyoming"

We crouched, Dennis and I, in a little cubby hole beneath the stage. It was almost time for the matinee performance. Dennis was demonstrating how to open and close the curtains that covered the screen. A large crank handle dug into the pit of my stomach. You turned it one way, the curtains opened; you turned it the other way, they closed again. Perfectly straightforward.

"Only we don't call them curtains, we call them 'tabs' instead. I don't know why ..." added Dennis hastily, "... you open the tabs when the adverts come on, and close them at the end of the big picture. We also usually open and close them between trailers, and the news reel and so on. But we'll skip all that today as you're new at the job."

"Thanks," I said "but how will I know when exactly to turn the handle?"

"Couldn't be simpler. See that little blue bulb over your head? I switch it on and off from the operating box as a signal. So, when you see it flash you turn the handle. It's dead easy."

"Thank goodness for that." I said, rising to leave and smashing the signal bulb and its holder to fragments with my shoulder.

"Christ! Now you've done it!" whispered Dennis. "We haven't any spares in the place. You'll just have to cope without it for now."

"But I can't. I know I'll muck it up!" I wailed.

"Look," said Dennis patiently "stop worrying. It's a doddle. You can just see the corner of the screen over your right ear, if you crane your neck a bit. When you see the adverts hit the screen, open the tabs, thats it!"

"What about closing them?"

"Ah, a bit more tricky." admitted Dennis.
"Hang on though ..." his face cleared "at the end of the film the feller and his bird go into a big clinch, there's a burst of romantic music as 'THE END' flashes on. When you hear that music, start closing the tabs, okay?"

"Okay." I said, doubtfully.

I followed Dennis back up to the operating box, passing on the way various members of the female staff who'd just arrived. Dennis seemed very popular with them all, quite the lady's man. As for me, I was almost pathologically shy.

I would blush bright crimson if I had to even speak to any member of the opposite sex - under age-sixty; even if it was only to ask for a box of matches and a quarter of jelly babies.

"Who are the others who work here?" I asked Dennis when we got back to the operating box. Dennis moved around the equipment, rapidly passing from one familiar task to another, with the ease of long experience. The houselights were switched on, the colourful proscenium lights (tab lights) adjusted to give a welcoming orange glow.
The amplifiers and other electrical equipment switched on and adjusted, records placed on the non-sync, the arc lamps prepared, the lenses polished and adjusted, the first reels of film threaded in the projectors. All done deftly but without

seeming haste, like an airline pilot going through his flight drill. While he worked, Dennis gave me a brief rundown on each of the other members of staff.

"Mr. Clapshaw, the manager - you've already met him: he's fair but he doesn't stand any nonsense. Actually, he can be very nasty when he likes. He works just as hard as we do, if not harder. He's determined to make this place pay, or to go bust in the attempt."

"Julia, his wife, she's the cashier: a nice, curly-headed little blonde, but as hard as nails when it comes to the business itself. She's just as determined as her old man to keep this dump a going-concern."

"Then there's Ernie the doorman. He only works here at night. He has a daytime job at the sausage factory up the road. His job is to lend a bit of tone to the place with his tatty uniform, and kick the Teds out when they get too rough.

In the bigger cinemas they have several full-time doormen, and they kill the fleas and whitewash the stair treads in their spare time. Here we have to do it instead. Oh, and Ernie is Mrs. Clapshaw's brother, by the way."

"There's also Aggie and Em, the two cleaners. You'll 'ave met them this morning; and of course there's Wally Tate the second Op. You'll meet him tomorrow."

"How about the usherettes?" I asked.

"There's three of 'em." replied Dennis with a grin. "There's Belinda Warren. She's a smashin' little blonde, she is. And there's Janet Donovan, a gorgeous brunette. I knock around with Belinda and Wally knocks around with Janet. They're both married of course (the girls that is) but their husbands don't understand them!"

"What about the third usherette?" I asked anxiously.

"That's old Lucy, Mr. Clapshaw's aunt ..." replied Dennis gravely.

"Anyway, I can't stand here talking all day, I'm off to the bog. You carry on playing records 'till I get back. We've still got quarter of an hour before the show starts."

Dennis clattered off downstairs, leaving me with a feeling of awful responsibility beside the non-sync. I played a random selection of music from the pile of scratchy 78s. These, kept by the side of the turntable, were for the entertainment of the half-dozen or so elderly patrons who always hobbled in, as soon as the doors opened.

I felt a lot happier than earlier in the day. True, I could scarcely be classed in the same bracket as Cecil B. de Mille or Sam Goldwyn, but I was at least now on the fringe of the entertainment industry; a small, but essential cog in a chain which stretched from the M.G.M. studios down to our fleapit patrons in the nine-penny stalls.

A raucous buzzer sounded close by my ear, interrupting my reverie and causing me to involuntarily leap into the air. It sounded again more insistently a few moments later just as, thankfully, Dennis appeared.

"Time to start," said Dennis laconically, starting up the arc lamp on number One Projector with a great fizz and splutter. "Go and do your stuff ... get a move on!"

I flew downstairs, racing through the auditorium; much to the consternation of the few old ladies in the audience, who looked around anxiously for evidence of fire or other catastrophe. Diving under the stage, I flung the handle round to open the 'tabs' just as the first advertisements hit the screen. The audience settled back thankfully to snooze the afternoon away, and I rejoined Dennis to be initiated into the art of rewinding film.

This task was by no means as straightforward as it sounded. Each spool of film was about two-thousand-feet in length, and had to be rewound back to the beginning after each showing; all while holding the film carefully between finger and thumb to check for any tears or damage. If you held the film too loosely, you might well miss a tear which could cause the film to snap during the next show (a black mark against the operator).

Hold the film too tightly and you finished up with a network of painful gashes where the film bit into your skin, like a high speed razor. Most trainee operators spent their first few weeks with very sore fingers.

Another problem: stopping the machine when you felt a tear in the film as you rewound it. Stop it too quickly and it would snap altogether; stop one reel slightly after the other and the film would go spiraling up in the air, and land in a complicated mess around your head and shoulders. You had to do the job just-right or you had endless trouble.

Mr. Clapshaw kept popping up to the box, every now and then, to help Dennis out with changing the film from one machine to the other. He had started as an operator himself and still helped out when anyone was off sick, or until another could be trusted to run a projector himself. On one of his visits, after glancing at me approvingly, as I perspired over the rewinding machine, he said "Philip, when you have finished that reel I want you to go over to Mantellini's, the ice cream people in Poulton Road. They've forgotten to send the choc-ices for the first house performance, so I want you to go and fetch them for me."

I later learned to dread the frequent occasions when Mantellini forgot to deliver our small consignment of ice cream (I was most often convinced that they just couldn't be bothered!). It would be my job to walk down to the ice cream wholesaler (many small cinemas like ours had not freezers of their own yet), then stagger back a mile or so to the cinema,

clutching the large, heavy container of vanilla tubs and choc-ices.
The real trouble was the dry ice. The ice creams had to be kept frozen for several hours after delivery, so they were packed in a container with dry ice cubes. As one carried it along, the metal case grew colder and colder to the touch, until frostbite became a real possibility. After a while I learned to always carry a pair of thick, woolly mitts round with me, especially during the summer; since the greater the heatwave, the more likely we were to suddenly run out of ice cream.

On this first occasion, I staggered into the cinema foyer with my fingers rapidly becoming icicles. As I stood there recovering my breath, I heard the burst of romantic theme music from the feature film! I recognised it from the bits Dennis had played over that morning. I must have taken longer getting back from Mantellini's than I realised! The film must be over! I dropped the case of ice creams on the marble foyer floor, with a tremendous crash, hurled myself through the dark auditorium and down into the little the cubby hole below the stage. Whirling the handle madly, I waited for the strains of "God Save the King" to herald the end of the programme ...

... Instead, a chorus of groans, and cries of execration from the audience, assailed my puzzled ears. No more than ten seconds later Dennis burst like a fire cracker into the cubby hole, whirling the handle back again to open the tabs.

"What the bloody hell made you do that?" he said in a hoarse whisper, when he could speak again.

"The theme music, the big clinch, the end of the film like you said!" I whispered back completely at a loss.

"You daft git!" hissed Dennis "This is only half way through the film! This is where they go into a clinch for the first time. Then she goes off with this other feller and he meets this ballet dancer, and then they both come together again at the end."

"How the heck was I supposed to know that?" I said indignantly.

"I dunno ..." Dennis whispered fiercely. "... all I do know is, if you ever do that again, I'll stuff a reel of film up your bum and set light to it!"

Back at home, we sat at the tea table munching fish paste butties ...

"Nu? How did it go this time?" asked my father, who seemed to always start a sentence with the old Yiddish interrogative interjection, 'nu'.

"So so. I made one or two little mistakes but I think I'm getting the hang of the job alright."

"And the usherettes?" asked Dad anxiously. "You know how your mother worries over nothing. They are homely, middle-aged respectable ladies I hope!"

"Mum needn't worry," I said, "two of them are already spoken for and the third one is the manager's old aunt Lucy."

"Good, good." said father, nodding in a satisfied manner. "Keep your mind on your job and you will be sure to get on. Have another fish paste sandwich?"

"No thanks," I said, "I must be off again."

It was nearly six O'clock. I thought of my old friends at the grocers shop, who would be home by now after their days' work. I was just half-way through mine.

I carried the tea things into the stone-floored scullery and dumped them in the earthenware sink. I put a few biscuits into a paper bag for later in the evening, then got my raincoat and cloth cap from the hook in the hall.

A little shower of loose plaster rained down as I brushed against the wall. The house really was in a terrible state of repair. The pre-war wallpaper bulged and hung in loose folds. The teapot-brown paintwork was flaking away, exposing in patches the greens and greys of long forgotten decoration.

A few threadbare scraps of carpet made little moth-eaten islands amid the stone flags and old floorboards. We seemed to exude an air of poverty and were destined to become poorer still over the next few years ...

I remembered the comfortable days before the war. The days when, despite the great depression, we still seemed to have enough money to keep a well furnished, spick-and-span home. The charlady, Mrs. Hill, came in every day to scrub the front steps, wax-polish the floors and Brasso the door sills. When the grocer, the greengrocer and the fishmonger, all brought their wares to the door, they would touch their caps to my mother, as if honoured by our custom. Of course, in those days we had no car, no washing machine or fridge, no hoover or phone.

We did have Mrs. Hill the char, who probably cost less to run and was decidedly more user-friendly. In place of the car and fridge, we made do with the No. 14 bus and the cold flagstones of the pantry respectively.

Nevertheless, we were well-off when compared to many of our neighbours - a comfortable, lower-middle class family living in a comfortable lower-middle class road; and I, health permitting, was to follow in Dad's footsteps in the tailoring business.

Unfortunately, life is full of surprises. When we returned to our house after a long absence during the war years, we found it stripped bare. It had been looted with seemingly expert thoroughness - hardly a single item of any value remained. By then, age and ill-health had reduced Dad's earning capacity to bare subsistence levels. There was no money to re-furbish or re-decorate, so we bought a in a few cheap oddments of second-hand furniture, cut up the one remaining large carpet into a number of smaller pieces and set up home again as best we could.

As for me and the tailoring business ... I had only myself to blame for my present pickle. I could have followed in Dad's footsteps. His interest and connections would have ensured a good opening in the trade. But, my stubborn hankering after a career in the electrical industry had been my undoing.

I pulled my peaked cap down to shield my face against the cold, windy March evening. I closed the front door behind me and walked up Liscard Road, where the feebly twinkling lights of the Kings Picture House invited me to the evening performance.

Reel Four

This Sunday only:

"Meet Miss Bobby Socks"

also

"Badman's Territory"

If ever I am deemed so wicked as to merit a place where the damned spend eternity shoveling nutty slack on to the fires of hell, the first sound I shall hear as the gates clang behind me will be the strains of Edward German's 'Merrie England.' This horribly boring old musical comedy, a particular favourite of Mr. Clapshaw's, was thought to lend a bit of upper-class tone to our programmes. So, at least once before each performance, we played a scratchy 78 rpm shellac record of selections from that ghastly show.

I must have heard the wretched thing five hundred times, at least, before the record mercifully wore out completely (at which point I was thankfully allowed to hurl it into the dustbin). I must have developed a sort of pathological allergy to it ... even now, sixty years later, the first few bars of that harmless piece ('where are the yeomen, the yeomen of England, tiddly pom, tiddly pom, ...) can bring me out in a psychological rash.

Although still a teenager, I had never been one for the Pops. My taste lay in the direction of classical music. If Mr. Clapshaw wanted a bit of tone in the record selection, why not give them Sibelius? I bought a record of Sibelius' tone poem 'Finlandia' on the petty cash and put it on ...

"Jesus wept!" groaned Wally and Dennis, "That's even worse than "Merrie bloody England!" and Dennis whipped the record off the turntable and hurled it, Discus fashion, into the waste bin. Realising I had been too adventurous, I set my sights lower when I managed to get Tchaikovsky accepted into our repertoire of interval music, (alongside the current middle-brow favourites of Charlie Kunz piano selections, and Reginald Forte at the organ of the Tower Ballroom Blackpool).

Back to my first day at the King's cinema ...

The dusk fell and the gas lamps flickered into life, as the little man on his bike rode along the street turning them on. I took up my post as disc-jockey at the non-sync playing 'Merrie England', Charlie Kunz, Reginald Forte, ..., and so on, while the first house audience trickled in. The buzzer gave its peremptory order to start the show and, without daring to look at Dennis, I went down and took up my position below the stage. Dennis had been busy repairing the signal light, after which it blinked reassuringly at all the right places. So I was able to open and close the tabs at all the right points in the show without a hitch.

That evening Mr. Clapshaw was kept too busy to help Dennis out at film changeover times. I rather resented this at the time, but Dennis said (with a hint of resignation in his voice), I had to start learning to run a projector some time or other, it might as well be now!

The procedure was such that when the film in one machine had run down to the last minute or so, the operator on duty bawled out "CHANGEOVER at the top of his voice. The other operator (who was rewinding film in the next room, doing his football pools or maybe just having a quiet smoke) would come rushing in to take over on the other machine, which he had previously loaded with the next reel of film to be shown.

The incoming operator's first task was to "strike up the arc"; that is, to touch together the two carbon rods inside the lamp house. On separating them, the brilliant white arc light would strike up with great spluttering and clouds of white smoke.

He then had to keep the rods just the right distance apart, to provide a clear black-and-white picture on the screen. If the rods were too far apart, the picture would turn blue and then go off altogether as the arc fizzled out. If the ends were too close the picture would go a horrible muddy brown colour.

As the rods burned away, they demanded constant attention. The surest way to judge a good operator was by the colour of his screen, or rather the lack of it in those black-and-white days. Each carbon rod lasted for about three reels of film, when the little bits of stub remaining had to be fished out and new rods inserted. Carbon rods were expensive and it was held a point of honour to burn the stubs down to the last possible fraction. Of course, if one overdid it, the rods could give out in the middle of a reel, blacking-out the picture to an audience chorus of hoots and groans (and with the manager certainly taking a leading role).

In all my subsequent years as an operator, I never completely lost the feeling of mild panic, while watching the last bit of carbon rod burn away; praying for the reel to end before it fizzled out completely.

Back to the drama of the changeover ...

Having got the arc lamp lit, the next step in changing reels was for both operators to watch the screen intently. A small, unobtrusive dot appeared at the top right-hand corner of the screen, just eight seconds from the end of the reel of film. The operator on the machine with the almost empty reel, screamed "RIGHT" at the top of his voice the very instant he saw it (in case his mate happened to blink at the crucial moment). The operator on the machine with the new reel of film then launched into a frenzied outburst of activity ...

First, the motor running the film would be switched on. Then, in the case of equipment as ancient as ours, the flywheel had to be thumped, kicked or otherwise accelerated to get it up-to-speed in time. Then, a lightning-quick check and adjustment of the arc lamp to make sure its colour was still dead white.

Flinging the steel safety shutter up out of the way in front of the arc lamp, the Op adopted the 'changeover stance.' This took the form of a letter 'X' - legs wide apart to keep you rock steady on your feet, one hand stretched out to grab the spring-loaded changeover shutters, the other stretched out to operate the sound changeover switch. Then, a second small dot appeared on the screen, just as the last few inches of film ran off the reel. A second scream of "RIGHT" and, in the same instant, pull the lever to close the shutter in front of the empty projector, and snap open a corresponding shutter in front of your own.

With the other hand a turn of the switch which swapped-over the sound on to his own machine ... and the changeover was complete!

A good pair of operators would take care to match the colour of their arc lights, while monitoring the sound levels and making sure there was exactly eight seconds-worth of blank film in the full machine (to match the eight seconds between changeover marks on the film). All this to avoid the risk of a gap between one reel ending and the next beginning; or equally annoying, an overlap between reels cutting off the actor mid-speech ... or causing the big kiss to be unconsummated.

A good operator would take care of all these details and, on average, a score of changeovers would take place during each day's programme; all with such smoothness that the audience would be quite unaware. Of course, this was precisely the idea of the whole complicated procedure. Unfortunately, high-spirited young operators, bored by the tedium of the job, would sometimes seize upon the tense moments of the film changeover to play practical jokes; especially when they were so fortunate as to have a gormless apprentice to test them on. Bursting paper bags or perhaps screaming "fire!" at the crucial moment, were quite routine tests of the nerves of the trainee operator.

After a few days of practice, I rather prided myself on the slickness of my changeovers. There I was, standing tense in the changeover posture; arms reaching out to the levers and my eyes glued to the distant screen. When suddenly, that stealthy swine Wally crept up behind me and dropped a pile of empty steel film cans onto the concrete floor ... an almighty, terrifying crash!

I leapt high in the air, with a strangled yelp and, by reflex action, sent the shutters changing over with a loud clang.

The mystified audience then saw the villain throw up his heels and tumble to the ground, but without any discernible cause. The hero's causative knockout punch having, on this occasion, not quite reached it's target. In response to my bitter protests all I got was, "It's all part of the training Phil. You must make sure you can handle distractions like this." Wally and Dennis collapsed sniggering while I retired to the rewind room to soothe my wounded pride with a glass of cream soda.

My first night at the 'Kings' saw the programme progress smoothly on it's way: the adverts, the Joe McDoakes comedy, Popeye cartoon and then the Pathe Newsreel. When the last was over and had been rewound, instead of flinging the reel into one of the steel fireproof storage bins along with the rest of the programme, Dennis flipped it into a small carrying case and held it out to me ...

"Get your coat on Phil and run along with this over to the 'Queens'. They're due to show this in half an hour's time so get your skates on! Wait while they run it, then dash back here with it. We'll want it for second house."

In those far off days, the public were not in such close touch with events in the big wide world as it is used to today. True, the radio news told them what was happening and photos in the daily papers showed them frozen fragments of events; but only in the cinema newsreel, could one actually see the news in action: the new Superliner going down the slipway, Arsenal winning the cup, the wiggling hips of the Blackpool bathing beauty contest, the waving budget bag of a grimly smiling chancellor Sir Stafford Cripps. However, all this bringing of vital, up-to-date news in action to the masses had its problems, especially for a small unimportant cinema circuit like ours.

The newsreel was filmed on the spot, edited and dispatched to the big city cinemas within a day or so of the events having taken place. 'Trouble was, by the time it got to be our turn to run it, the news could well be two or three weeks old!

You might be taken to the scene of a recent big robbery, which apparently has the police completely baffled, and yet know from the daily papers that the criminals have been traced, captured, tried, found guilty and already put away for five years!

Another problem for the small exhibitor was the expense of hiring newsreels. This was partly solved, as in our case, by pairs of small cinemas like ours sharing one copy of each newsreel. The programme times at the respective cinemas would be adjusted so that when the first had shown its newsreel, there was just enough time for the junior projectionist to run or cycle with it to the other for showing there. In my case, as I had never learned to ride a bike, it would have to be a smart run there and back.

We shared our newsreel with the quaint, old-fashioned 'Queens' cinema a mile or so up the road in Poulton, near the Birkenhead docks. The Queens was of course larger than our own Kings (it had to be!), but in some respects it was little more than an interesting example of industrial archaeology; which, by some miracle, had managed to survive from some remote past when bioscopes and 'electric palaces' were all the rage (electric palaces were the very earliest Edwardian cinemas).

I arrived panting in the foyer of the Queens clasping the urgently-required newsreel in its fire-proof case. While I looked around for someone who could direct me to the operating box, a very ancient doorman dozed peacefully on his own particular seat in the corner. In the pay-box, a little grey-haired old lady nodded over some shapeless knitting.

It was very quiet and peaceful, with no sound but the faint snores of the doorman, the occasional click of the knitting needles and the wheezing of my own breath after running a mile or so to avoid being late.

Rapping on the pay desk ... "P-please, which way to to the operating box?" I wheezed. The old lady put down her knitting and, looking at me over her spectacles ...

"Good gracious young man, you do look warm ..." she said. "... you mustn't rush about so much you know. You young people! I don't know, you're all the same, rushing here, dashing there ..."

"The operating box, please?" I put in.

"Oh there's plenty of time for that - a good ten minutes before the news is due on. The box is through that door and up the steps, but sit down and have five minutes rest first." Thanking her hurriedly, I suggested that I'd better go up now to be on the safe side.

Unlike our own cinema, the Queen's had no balcony, being built on the tunnel plan - a long and narrow arched-roof auditorium, with the operating box situated just over the foyer. From my point of view this had the great advantage of fewer stairs to climb after my headlong dash through the streets.

Pushing open the operating box fire door, I was greeted by a bone-shaking, head-numbing racket that almost seemed to fling me out into the passage again. The projectors there made our own elderly machines look like the latest deluxe models. They were of such ancient vintage that they still had the synchronised turntables attached for the 1920s type talkies.

The machinery was unenclosed, without any attempt at sound-proofing or concessions to the safety of the operator. The sharp, steel anti-flicker blades whirled around in the open - quite ready to slice off the ear or finger of any careless projectionist.

The continuous roar made by the machines rendered even shouted communication near-impossible. The 'chief', Bert Morecambe, straightened up from the task of lacing one of the projectors. He mouthed some friendly conversation, which I could not interpret. I just smiled and nodded. A little bent figure of a man, he looked a good deal older than his probable real age. I learned he had been in the business since the days of silent films. After being exposed to this shattering level of noise seven hours a day, for perhaps thirty years, he was now stone deaf. But he could lip read quite well.

I handed over the newsreel, and he signed for me to follow him outside the box, whereupon he closed the door, thankfully shutting out the din.

"You want to watch your ears son!" he said in the style of loud voice only the deaf seem to manage. "The new machines they have nowadays are a hell of a lot quieter than those clattering Claras in there, but they're still not half quiet enough. You mark my words lad, you'll get a bit hard of hearing like me if you stay in this job long enough."

He was right too ... "Pardon?"

I trotted back to the King's through the now dark and empty streets. With the newsreel clutched affectionately to my bosom, it was 21:15 and I was beginning to feel a bit peckish. I snatched a surreptitious biscuit or two at the rewind bench, between spells of duty at the projector, and I wondered if it could be possible that all my future films would be as boring as this 'Badman's Territory'. It was perhaps just as well I didn't know the truth, as many of them would be a bloody sight worse!

At 22:30 the last 'baddie' hit the deck and the film dragged thankfully to its conclusion. I plodded down to the cubbyhole below stage to close the tabs for the last time that day - on a striking portrait of HM King George VI, surrounded by all the flags of Empire fluttering in the breeze. The house lights went up, the footlights went out, the small audience coughed and shuffled into their overcoats. We checked that all the electrical equipment had been turned off, and likewise all the dozen or so gas heaters around the hall. While helping the usherettes put up the seats we, most importantly, checked that no incontinent patron was left behind in the loo before locking up.

"Monday night ..." muttered Dennis as he donned his overcoat. "... usually comparative religion, unless it's politics, and the misdoings of the Labour Party - you can never tell with him."

"Eh?" I said blankly.

"You'll see." said Dennis grimly.

We put out the lights and, thankfully, left the dark and airless operating box for the cool night air.

Outside on the foyer steps Mr. Clapshaw waited for us alone. Mrs. Clapshaw had gone home early as soon as the last of the latecomers had paid for their tickets. It seemed that Mr. Clapshaw lived only a short distance away. It was the custom for those operators who (myself included) also lived in that general direction, to walk along with him.

"Well Philip," said Mr. Clapshaw brightly, "I'm sure we have done very well today and I know Dennis is very pleased with your progress."

Dennis grunted inaudibly as if in a hopeless attempt to discourage further conversation, but It was useless.

Then Mr. Clapshaw, after one or two preliminary verbal canters into my probable future with the firm, and the ruinous increase in the price of choc-ices, launched into a single-handed tour de force on comparative religion:

The Jews, the Muslims, the Sikhs ... what their religion did for them, how their customs were derived, and so on. His small captive audience listened, but were not expected to take part in his discourse ...

At the corner of his street, bleak and gaslit, we stopped; but the talk went on and on, till my head was spinning. He did a kind of grave little hop from one leg to the other, as he grew excited. His toothy white smile flashed every now and again in the lamp-light, whenever he expected a nod of agreement, touching some point in his argument. He was well-informed and had a good command of logic and rhetoric. He would have made a fine orator, but we were tired, bored and did not even wish to understand what he was saying.

We only wanted to get home, have a bite to eat and get to bed. As Mr. Clapshaw paused for a moment, to strike a light for his fag on the nearby lamp post, Dennis hissed to me in desperation, "Christ, when will the bugger run himself out of words? I want to get home!" While I thought this disrespectful, it did rather echo my own feelings.

I got home just before midnight to find Dad was still waiting up for me ...

"I was worried about you ..." he said, handing me a mug of hot cocoa. "... I thought the show finished at ten-thirty."

"Mr. Clapshaw, the manager," I said, taking a sip of cocoa "he gave us a long talk on religion." Dad was clearly impressed and very interested. "So, your Mr. Clapshaw seems to be a very learned man. What did he say? What does he think about our religion?"

"I was too tired to take in a single word" I replied, draining the cup and rising to go up to bed.

And that, I am afraid, was to be the fate of most of Mr. Clapshaw's future sermons.

Reel Five

Monday and Tuesday this week:

"Gay Senorita"

also

"Hell Ship Morgan"

Mr. Herbert Adolphus Gimble was a plump, balding little man with a tiny moustache and a deep, well-founded distrust of all projectionists. His principal job was that of company accountant for the small chain of cinemas (Hyman Bloom Enterprises Ltd) to which we belonged. He sat for most of the time in his little Hope Street office, under the gaunt sandstone shadow of Liverpool cathedral, and fought the desperate and never-ending battle to keep the company solvent. However, once or twice a week he would leave his bills and ledgers behind and, putting on his relief manager's outfit (threadbare evening suit, dress shirt, pearl studs and a worried expression), set off for one of the company's cinemas to release the manager there on his day off.

Mr. Gimble, although an able administrator and first-class accountant, was blessed with a profound ignorance regarding technical matters. All he knew was that, whenever anything went wrong with the mysterious workings of a cinema equipment, it always seemed to cost a fortune to put right; completely upsetting his books, and just when he was within an ace of balancing them. In this respect he was a bit like the impecunious owner of a battered old family saloon; dreading to hear that his cherished banger requires a series of expensive repairs to keep it on the road.

The projectionists looked forward to Mr. Gimble's visits with keen anticipation, warmly welcoming him on his appearance at their cinema. His distrust of the breed meant that Mr.

Gimble did not reciprocate. Nonetheless, Dennis and Wally would go to surprising lengths to ensure that Gimble was well-entertained on his visits to the 'Kings'.

In celebration of one particular visit they dressed up the spare projector mechanism with bits of rusty wire, and other rubbish, until it looked like a worthless lump of scrap iron. Carrying it ostentatiously past the open office door, they talked in gloomy stage whispers about a total write-off ... that it would take six months to get a replacement ... and that the model had probably been discontinued anyway. It would mean a whole new projector, costing around £2,000 - £3,000, heaven forbid! Mr. Gimble started up from his desk with a howl of dismay, while Wally and Dennis collapsed with laughter at the poor man's expense. They would certainly have been fired for such behaviour, had it been possible to procure replacements willing to work for the miserably low salaries paid by our struggling company.

On another occasion, they called Gimble up to the operating box and informed him, with grave faces, that something serious had happened: Number One projector had packed up completely (this, ten minutes before an almost packed second-house was due to start). Dennis flicked the projector motor switch to demonstrate the fault and at once an acrid cloud of grey smoke billowed out from the machine. "Try it for yourself Mr. Gimble," said Dennis sadly "I'm afraid you'll have to give the crowd their money back."

Ashen-faced, Gimble flicked the switch as he was bidden and another even denser cloud of smoke erupted from the machinery, half engulfing the little man and causing him to cough and whoop spasmodically. He whispered despairingly "Good God! There must be at least two-hundred people out there. What am I to tell Mr. Bloom, the owner? Oh dear, dear ..." This was altogether too much for Wally. Until now he had been hidden behind the machine, puffing cigarette smoke into it through through a rubber tube. He appeared purple-faced and suppressing laughter, while an outraged Gimble stormed upstairs threatening to report us.

I had first bumped into Mr. Gimble one morning, a few days after starting at the 'Kings'. I was hurrying along with a large bucket of whitewash to paint the stair treads, when Gimble barely escaped becoming an involuntary prototype for the 'Man in a White Suit' (a popular film of the day). I apologised and introduced myself.

"Pleased to meet you Philip." said Gimble, quickly recovering his customary air of cheerful efficiency.

"Glad to see you working hard. Mr. Bloom likes to see enthusiasm on the part of his employees. Dedication and efficiency, that's what we ... AAARGH!"

Before my startled eyes Mr. Gimble seemed to be having several kinds of fit all at once. He rolled his eyes and pointed speechlessly up at the balcony. I followed his gaze to see Dennis and Wally striding along the four-inch wide balcony parapet, wielding cleaning mops as balancing poles. Then I remembered, we had run a circus film last night and Wally had bet Dennis five bob that he couldn't run along the edge of the balcony.

"Allez oop!" called out Wally triumphantly in emulation of the tightrope walker in the film.

"Stop that, you pair of stupid, idle tit-brained buggers. Come down out of that at once, or you're both fired!" barked Mr. Gimble.

Mr. Gimble's lapse into such impolite speech was highly atypical, but then he was badly shaken. Had the two lads missed their footing and tumbled headlong into the stalls twenty-five feet below, repairs to the backs of several seats might have been necessary, not to mention the cost of dry cleaning the blood stains off the seat covers. He sank back in a stalls seat and mopped his brow, as Dennis and Wally climbed sheepishly down. "I hope Philip ..." said Mr. Gimble sternly recovering "... that I never catch you doing such a stupid and dangerous trick as that."

"Mr. Gimble," I replied with a very real shudder "I could no more run along that parapet up there, than I could do a simultaneous juggling act with the two-thousand, one-hundred and ninety-six peas which I happen to know are in Mr. Clapshaw's jar today!"

I was, and in fact still am, one of the biggest cowards in existence. I don't mind admitting that when it comes to leaping across ditches, climbing trees, jumping off walls, balancing on narrow ledges or similar feats of daring ... I'm the chap who backs away grinning foolishly, muttering something about "being delighted to have a go if not for the sudden stitch in my side." I trace the origins, of this abject cowardice, back to a childhood strange enough in some respects to have formed the subject of one of Franz Kafka's weird novels.

I was an only-child and a very sickly one at that, lurching from one malady to the next with a persistence worthy of a better cause. My parents worked themselves up into such a neurotic state of concern over my health, that their carryings-on were almost beyond belief. I was never allowed out of doors unless the sun was cracking the pavement. In winter, I was confined indoors, made to don a heavy tweed overcoat and leggings, just to cross our draughty hallway to the loo. I wore flannel undershirts, flannel body belts and long woollen underwear. I was made to drink foul-tasting herbal preparations by the gallon, and my sole diet consisted of milk pudding and steamed fish.

However, this was all minor stuff compared with my parents more serious errors of judgement. Since schools were notoriously cold and draughty places, and the diet there might well include anything but steamed fish and milk pudding, the apparently obvious remedy was to not send me to school at all.

For nine years my parents succeeded in fending-off school attendance officers, while I stayed at home. Mum was very good at English and taught me to read and write quite well.

Poor Dad, who came from Polish peasant stock, could barely read English himself, so taught me his repertoire of Yiddish music hall songs (his contribution to an already very limited curriculum). With this unusual syllabus, augmented by the excellent schools broadcasts on the radio, I had to rest content until I was almost fourteen-years-old.

My parents also kept me in a wheelchair all this time. I suffered a lot with asthma and they were afraid that, if I were allowed to run round like other children, I might "overdo things" and bring on an attack. As I matured, my wheelchairs were bigger and heavier, requiring Mum and Dad's combined efforts to push me around. As I dreamed up plans to motorise the thing, to save my parents a hernia each, I don't think the absurdity of being in the chair ever entered my mind ... all this time I could walk around perfectly well! It was just that I was far too obedient, ever to question my parents misguided eccentricities.

Having moved to Wales for the duration of the war, by the time I was fourteen I had begun a desultory attendance at a little Welsh village school. The school was half-way up a hillside behind the village, so the kids took it in turns to push me to and from school in the last and largest of my wheelchairs. Once I got to school I would hop out, the wheel chair would be parked somewhere and I would tear around the playground with the rest of the children. Now and again, I got to thinking that something didn't add up somewhere but I couldn't quite put my finger on it.

The issue was finally settled thanks to the sporting instincts of Stinky Hughes and Drip-Nose Thomas, whose turn it was to push me up the hill one day.

They were determined to set a new land-speed-record in getting me from Daft Megan's sweet shop, to Icky Morgan's builders yard; which represented a statutory Welsh mile. Unfortunately, their enthusiasm outran their navigational abilities ... we skidded off the road, landing me in Mrs. Evans front-garden. I was unhurt, but the wheel chair was a total write-off. Horrified, Stinky and Drip-Nose were about to commandeer Mrs. Evans' wheelbarrow, in an effort to complete the journey. "Don't worry," I said reassuringly "I'm quite okay."

I gathered up the bits of wheelchair, flung them onto Icky Morgan's scrap-metal heap and strode cheerfully along with the boys up the hill to school. I heard no more about wheelchairs after that but went about happily like a normal human being on two legs rather than four squeaky wheels.

And so, I eventually entered my working life with a number of inherited handicaps. These were not so much due to prolonged ill-health, but more to my parents' well-intentioned, but dreadfully misconceived attempts to avert it. I was painfully shy, awkward and clumsy in my movements, a great coward and thoroughly naive. It was to the great credit of Dennis and Wally that they took little advantage of me. Rather, they tried in their rough way to bring me on wherever they could.

In this respect, the second Op., Wally Tate, was the more effective tutor. Wally was a lean, agile lad of almost nineteen. He affected a bushy RAF-style moustache and, as has been seen already, was gifted with a keen but slightly wicked sense of humour. But, he was more thoughtful and perceptive than Dennis; able to help me out of some of my many problems, without causing me to clam up mentally (as Dennis' jovial heavy-handed attempts were apt to do).

"Look here Phil ..." Wally would say "if the Judies could see you now, tottering down the stairs sideways and holding on to the rails, as if Niagara falls was below you, they'd split their sides laughing. Just say to yourself "I am not going to fall" and walk down normally like a sensible person. That's it, now you're shaping up." Dennis would probably have just given me a shove in the back and yelled "Walk down properly you daft bugger!"

Despite this banter, there were some jobs I just could not do. Lamp maintenance for example: you had to climb to the top of a rickety ladder to clean the fittings and change any dud bulbs. I would totter about eight foot above the ground as though all eternity stretched beneath me, and my bony knees would rattle like castanets. Dennis and Wally would hoot with laughter and suggest I take a parachute up with me for safety. But it was no use, I just could not do it. Wally would take over and I would be given a safe ground-level job; such as taking a rag and a tin of scouring powder to erase the rude poems and illustrations from the Ladies and Gents toilet walls.

When I had done this, and maybe whitewashed the stairs and sprayed the fleas off the back seats, Mr. Clapshaw's very pretty wife, Julia, would commandeer me to advance my education in the matters of high finance. She would stuff the pockets of my old sports jacket with the previous couple of days takings (maybe some £50 or more in notes and small change), stuff the paying-in book into my top pocket and steer me in the direction of the local Midland bank to deposit the cash. Luckily all this took place in a naive era, before such noble wealth-sharing activities as street muggings became commonplace.

So, apart from making my jacket pockets even more shapeless than usual, I suffered no ill-effects. As a loyal staff member, I was pleased when the takings were bigger than usual.

When my pocket bulges were particularly small, I would feel depressed thinking of poor Mr. Gimble and how upset he would be when he learned how little we had paid in. I felt vaguely guilty on such occasions, as though somehow it was my fault for not paying in a larger amount. I took things very seriously for a lad of sixteen.

Now Dennis and Wally were just the opposite, life was one big joke to them. They never missed an opportunity for horseplay and larking about generally, not least on

Clapshaw's day off and when the luckless Gimble would have to bear the brunt of any consequences. On one occasion, about two months after I started at the Kings, we were running a medieval horse opera (complete with knights in armour, jousting at the lists and damsels in distress). It was a lousy film of course, but Dennis and Wally were delighted with it, discussing it's finer points most enthusiastically.

"There's only one thing I didn't like about it ..." objected Wally, "when that daft twit in the crimson armour went charging down the lists, with his lance waving around like a brollie - dead stupid, that's what it was, dead stupid ... !"

"Alright then," said Dennis hotly "how would you have done it?"

Wally grabbed hold of a broom handle, thrust a mop into my hands and leapt lightly onto Dennis' unsuspecting shoulders ...

"Right, Dennis old son, I'll show you the proper way to hold a lance."

He flourished the broom handle fiercely and, digging his heels into Dennis's back, gave a blood-curdling whoop. The pair instantly charged down upon me, as I stood horseless by the rewind room door. I saw a very real chance of being pinned to the door like an entomologists beetle, so at the very last instant, I stepped aside and flung open the rewind room door ... the pair went charging through, only to run full-tilt into Mr. Gimble, who had just arrived at the other side. He howled as the lads combined momentum carried them across the rewind room, followed by an almighty thud. They finished up in a tangled heap by the film bins.

"You daft pair of buggers, what the 'ell do you think you're playing at?" screamed a traumatised Gimble.

Apologising profusely, the boys dusted Mr. Gimble down, found his spectacles and straightened the frames, sitting him down on the rewind room seat. I offered him a cup of my cream soda to restore his nerves, but he waved it away in speechless indignation ...

When he had recovered, he said in an ominous tone "Mr. Mills, you will kindly come into my office immediately. I wish to talk to you on a serious matter." Gimble turned on his heel and limped downstairs ...

We looked at each other with discomposure; Evidently we had gone too far this time and were well and truly in for it.

Dennis, taking a deep breath, followed Gimble downstairs to Clapshaw's office, while Wally and I got on with preparing the programme.

To our astonishment, ten minutes later Dennis returned wearing a grin, which threatened to split his jovial face in two.

"I've got the Garston job lads, £4 a week. I'm to start in eight weeks-time, when old Sam Pomfries retires!"

The announcement took us completely by surprise. Of course, we had heard rumours about old Sam being due retirement, and since the position was also rumoured to carry a salary as high as £4 a week, it had created a ripple throughout our small circuit of cinemas. The Garston Picture House was a great, seedy barn of a place. Stuck in a drab down-town area, the position of chief there was a good promotion; well worth having for someone young like our Dennis. We broke into a babble of congratulations and slapped Dennis heartily on the back, for we were genuinely pleased at his promotion.

"Hey," said Wally, as a thought struck him "what happens here when you go?"

"Oh, I forgot to mention," said Dennis grinning "you're to take my place as chief. Gimble wants to see you next, and young Phil here takes over from Wally as Second Op. They'll be advertising for a new trainee op next week."

Mum was home from Deva hospital by now, and I proudly told her and Dad that night.

"I've got a promotion already! I'll be getting a rise to thirty-five-shillings-a-week and it's a very responsible position. I'll actually be in charge of running the show when Wally is off!"

"Very good," said my father, nodding approvingly "you'll be manager one day if you just have patience."

By now, Mum had given up her efforts to persuade me to leave the cinema business (she should have kept right on trying!). She added her congratulations, although was unable to resist adding that my new wage, would be no more than I got as a grocer's boy for far fewer hours and easier work ...

With Mum home again, thankfully we could dispense with my father's best culinary efforts. We returned to a normal, sensible diet of steamed fish, potatoes and boiled tapioca pudding. At meal times I would sometimes wistfully recall a spell I had in hospital a year or so earlier. The discomforts associated with hospitalisation, passed almost unnoticed in the tremendous discovery of such rare delicacies as fried sausages, meat pies, fish and chips, and steamed pudding. I ate until I almost burst, without suffering any ill-effects whatsoever. I believe that, if I had been run over by a bus one day, outside the steps of the 'Kings', I should have been discovered with an ecstatic smile, all the way the to hospital. Not in delirium, but buoyed-up by visions of heaping-great plates of fried fish and chips, followed by treacle pudding!

Reel Six

All this week:

"The Adventures of Rusty"

also

"Cassidy of Bar 20"

There were surprisingly few Jewish people in this country and cinema operators were also a comparatively rare breed. The combination of a Jewish cinema operator is therefore one of general uniqueness. In fact, I calculated that in 1949 there could have been no more than 1.5 Jewish cinema operators in the whole country; and I was lucky enough to be the whole one! Who the other half-one was I never discovered. He could perhaps have been only half-Jewish, or only a part -time operator, but that is mere speculation. The basis of my calculation was quite simple:

There were about 15,000 operators in the country. The Jewish contingent of the British population was just under 1%. Of these, not one Jewish family in a hundred would have dreamed of allowing their son to follow such a strange profession. Tailoring, yes ... cabinet making, salesman ... possibly; Lawyer, doctor, international concert pianist - please God we should be so lucky! But cinema operator? Oy! What mishigas, what foolishness.
Okay, so 15,000 divided by 100, divided by 100 again gives us the 1.5 Jewish cinema operators aforesaid.

I can't say I ever encountered much in the way of racial prejudice at work, or that being Jewish stood in the way of my career; except that Mr. Clapshaw, and his successors, always made a great fuss when I insisted on having time off to attend Synagogue for the Jewish New year ...

"Of course Philip" Mr. Clapshaw would say on these occasions "We don't mind you being a Jew. Why should we? But you really must not let your religion affect your working life in this way. It's most irregular. What if the Catholics on our staff asked to have every saints day off? I should be left to run the place by myself!"

"It's only two days a year Mr. Clapshaw." I would reply doggedly "So I should like to have next Monday and Tuesday off please. Anyway, Tuesday's my regular day-off so it's only one extra day."

No doubt priding himself on his extreme racial tolerance, Mr. Clapshaw would give in with a sigh.

Not that I was much of a Yid to start with. True, Dad had always been a pious and observant Orthodox Jew and Mum, although a bit of an agnostic, had always kept a Kosher home for him. But my early ill-health, during my formative years, had kept me away from attending 'Cheder' (Jewish religion classes). Evacuation to our wartime home in a Welsh village, miles from any synagogue, left me with a very tenuous hold on the Jewish faith.

Like many Jews in similar situations, I worked out a set of working compromises between my natural careless inclinations on the one hand, and my wish to not offend my parents on the other. I whirled the bacon slicer at the Maypole grocery stores, but would not dream of sampling it's contents. I worked on Saturdays (the Jewish sabbath) but took time off for Yom Kippur (the day of atonement). If I could do it surreptitiously, I was quite partial to the odd non-kosher sausage when I could get one.

However, if I could afford to be picky regarding which of the 613 Jewish religious laws I would follow, and which I would ignore, I had no such option when it came to the one-thousand or so rules and practices, that went into making an experienced cinema operator. Dennis would be leaving us shortly and I would have my work cut out, becoming fully proficient as a second projectionist, after so recently starting in the business as a raw recruit. So far I had done little but act the part of spotty-faced Cinderella, to Dennis and Wally (the ugly sisters). Cleaning, scrubbing, fetching and carrying, running errands and doing all the muckiest jobs.

Now suddenly, all this was to change. To continue the analogy, fairy Gimble had waved his magic wand and, hey-presto, in eight weeks time, I was to turn into a highly trained technician. I should be able to run a complete cinema programme, strip down and repair the projectors and, in general, know how everything electrical in the cinema worked, knowing how to put it right if it didn't! There really was a hell of a lot to learn and not so many weeks left in which to become proficient.

Take for a start the regular task of making up a new programme. Just one item on the curriculum, but a significant art in itself. A task which left very little room for error.

Films were collected and delivered in the early hours of the morning, by the black sinister-looking vans of the FTS (film transport service). Each driver had the keys for all the cinemas on his round, calling at each one several times a week. He would to pick up all the old programmes and deposit the new.

A complete two-and-a-half-hour programme of films in steel-lined fireproof packing cases, which might weigh upwards of 100 lbs. In our case, we had to lug these up and down our steep spiral staircase, from the rewind room to the foyer and back, five times a week. Once for each change of programme. It usually took me three or four exhausting journeys to get a complete programme upstairs. Dennis, by comparison, would simply balance all the cases on top of each other and actually run upstairs with them.

Now and then it happened that, when we came to check a delivery, we would find we were a film short. Frantic phone calls would ensue, usually ending up in me being given a shilling or two out of petty cash, and told to go over to Seacombe ferry terminus to pick up a substitute copy. The expense of a taxi was unthinkable and the films were too much of a fire risk to be allowed on buses. So, I would be faced with carrying a packing case weighing up to 30 lbs or more on my aching shoulder for a couple of miles across town.

I developed a negative Pavlovian reaction to the sight of those films, which I had been forced to carry in this way; and heartily detested them without any reference to their artistic merit. I can imagine even the most ardent film critic would have changed his opinion of such a classic as 'Gone With the Wind' had he ever lugged it on his shoulders, from our local station to the cinema, where it was anxiously anticipated.

Once the new films had been hauled up to the rewind room, and checked-off against the printed programme, they had to be wound onto spools, and checked for any damage from their last showing. Following some horrific conflagrations in the early days, involving many fatalities, stringent safety regulations were in force. Reels of film had to be no more than 1,000 ft long and transported in fire-proof cases. Operating boxes were to be built of stone or brick, with steel self-closing doors. In the event of a sudden fire, while it was true that the operators themselves would almost certainly be roasted to a cinder before their escape, at least the audience would have time to get out to safety.

"Isn't this safety palaver a bit overdone?" I asked Dennis skeptically one day. "The film can't be all that dangerous surely?"

"It's made from nitro-cellulose, like a sort of incendiary bomb mixture." answered Dennis. "Come outside and we'll do a demo."

He grabbed a handful of scrap film and I followed him up onto the flat concrete roof. He dropped the film scraps into a metal bucket and lit a match.

"Stand well back!" warned Dennis.

As the match flame touched the film, it went off with a loud 'whoompf' and a sheet of flame at least eight feet high leapt out of the bucket. An instant later it was gone, and the bucket was quite empty. I went back into the rewind room without a word ... utterly convinced. From that day on, I treated nitro-cellulose film stock with the very respect it deserved, and was heartily glad when acetate safety film was introduced a few years later.

In making up a new programme, one started naturally enough with the adverts (which were silent in those days). Now, more than sixty-years later, these are still produced by Pearl & Dean. Each advert was paid for so many weeks showing. At the end of that time an Ad would be cut out and a new one stuck in its place. The same thing applied to the 'trailers'. For each programme, one had to cut out the old trailers and put new ones in their place, making sure that all went in the correct date sequence. Then the shorts (such as a Micky Mouse cartoon, or a Three Stooges comedy) and feature film had to be assembled and checked for any tears or bad joints.

These joints in the film were the bane of our existence. Wherever a film became torn or damaged, the torn ends had to be cut square and the ends overlapped and neatly stuck together with cement. The lucky operators in the big city cinemas who got their copies first, fresh from the suppliers, scarcely saw a repaired film in their lives. But, by the time the films reached us, they were just one stage away from the junk yard; often riddled with hundreds of joints - good, bad and atrocious.

We were supposed to check every single one. But I suppose it was inevitable that, now and again, a bad joint would slip through unnoticed. Then, the film would break during the performance, to a chorus of moans and hoots from the audience. No operator could hope to catch every single fault in an old film; there were only three hours available to make up a programme of around 15,000 feet of film. One naturally became somewhat fatalistic, when the boos and catcalls came you took it in your stride. After all, we mostly ran a perfect show ... but the audience would never applaud the competent projectionist!

I also rapidly became adept in the use of so-called 'blooping ink'. When you made a joint in the film, the sound track at that point made an annoying 'bang' as it whizzed through the projector. One got around this problem by shading around each joint with thick black ink. We called this stuff blooping ink, because if you did the job skillfully, the worst you heard as it ran through the machine was a gentle 'bloop'.

As you sorted out the various spools and odd bits of film, cutting and splicing joints as you went, the scope for catastrophe in a moment's inattention was considerable. You could, if not careful, put the odd reel in back-to-front, so all the actions happened in reverse, upside-down or left-to-right, or in the wrong order altogether. I was careless enough to do this once and actually got away with it. The mediocre film in question was improved beyond all recognition by having Reels Five and Seven inadvertently shown, but in the wrong order. The 'clever flashback sequence' was much commented-on by the patrons as they left. Admirers of the film said they enjoyed it much more at the Kings, than when they had seen it first at the city cinema. Not the sort of trick one could hope to get away with twice though ...

Having seen me safely over the hurdles of the projector, and the rewind room, Dennis and Wally felt it part of their tutorial duty to take my social life in-hand.

"Supposing Phil ..." said Dennis, one evening in hypothetical vein. "Supposing you got this Judy to go up a jigger with you, what would you do next?"

"No idea." I answered truthfully "What are you supposed to do?"

Dennis and Wally looked at each-other gloomily. Teaching me the use of blooping ink had been child's play compared with this assignment.

"Look," said Dennis after a moment's intense thought ...

"I can see we'll have to start you off with some elementary stuff. Wally and I are taking Belinda and Janet for a walk along the prom after the show tonight. You come along and we'll make a start on your education."

Belinda and Janet were the usherettes.

"I really don't think I should ..." I began nervously.

"That wasn't an invitation, that was an order!" said Dennis with a cheeky grim smile.

One never argued with Dennis.

It was a beautiful starlit evening. The lights of the great city across the river sparkled on the water. Ferry boats glided to-and-fro like luminous water beetles. The only sounds were the soft lapping of wavelets against the shore, and the hoot-hoot of a distant tugboat. The faint smell of the open sea wafted in from Liverpool bay. All rather romantic I suppose.

Dennis and Belinda, Wally and the other usherette, Janet, walked along arm-in-arm, whispering and giggling to each other. I trotted along behind feeling as out-of-place as a budgie in a cat rescue centre. I hoped the girls knew that it wasn't my idea to come along like this ...

"Right, this will do fine." said Dennis, stopping suddenly and citing a deep shadowy shelter facing the river. "In there all of you."

We sat down in a row and Dennis adopted a tutorial tone.

"Now then young Phil, here's Belinda - a right smashing bit of stuff as you can see. Now, let me see you give her a real proper kiss!"

I bent forwards, put my hands on Belinda's shoulders and, shutting my eyes pecked her somewhere on the cheek.

"No, no, no Phil!" said Dennis, thumping the arm of the seat in annoyance. "Watch this ..."

He grabbed Belinda around the waist and gave her a searing kiss, that seemed to last about ten minutes.

"Now," he said, rather purple in the face, panting a little "you-you do it like that!"

"But Dennis," I objected "she's your girl and I'd feel too embarrassed."

The fact that Belinda was married anyway, with two young children, never seemed to enter either of our minds, for some reason.

"Honestly, I'd be much too embarrassed. If I had a girl of my own it might be different, but I haven't." I said.

Dennis' face began to turn an alarming shade of purple, as he struggled to give vent to his pent up emotions. True, I was only sixteen, but the circles within which Dennis and Wally moved, that was quite old enough for a lad to know what's what.

Janet rose to her feet suddenly to break the tension.

"Come on you lot," she called cheerfully "lets walk along the shore and throw stones in the water."

I rose with a sense of relief, walking along with Wally and the girls down the shadowy seaweed-encrusted steps, on to the shore and along by the riverside, towards the distant twinkling lights of New Brighton pier. We tossed pebbles into the water, watching the reflected lights of the city break up into a million fragments with each expanding ripple. Dennis walked behind us, his face gloomy but resolved. He had evidently not given up hope of making a man of me ...

Opposite our cinema was Waterworth's greengocer's shop, where I called each afternoon to get a supply of apples and cream soda pop for us all at break times.

Serving behind the serried ranks of melons and spring onions, were Betty and Doris - all purple nail varnish, plucked eyebrows and daunting sophistication. Young Sue, a dark-haired tomboyish girl of about my own age, was there too. I made a point of being served by her, and even got to the astonishing height of being able to ask her for a "pound of best-eating-apples and a b-bottle of cream soda" without even blushing, or lapsing into complete incoherency.

I was foolish enough to mention this fact to my colleagues one night, when they immediately pounced upon it as an omen of considerable promise. Dennis darted off at once to the pay box and returned with wad of complimentary tickets ...

"Come on Phil," he said "we'll strike while the iron is hot, so to speak."

Dennis dragged me across the road and, in no time at all, chatted up the two older girls. They were all giggles and flattered to be taken notice of by such a great, handsome bloke as Dennis.

"Right." said Dennis later that night, like a sergeant reviewing his troops. "Have you got all the arrangements clear? The girls, all three of them, will be coming in for the second-house on our comp. tickets. Afterwards, when we have stripped off, we walk them home."

"How do you mean 'stripped off.' We can't walk through the streets with nothing on!" I interjected, aghast at this novel form of courtship which Dennis seemed to suggest.

Dennis banged his head twice sharply against the steel fireproof door, paused for a moment, then continued calmly ...

"Afterwards, when we have stripped the film off the spools and packed them away (today being the last day of our present programme), we walk the girls home. When we get too the jigger by Buchanan road, we split up. I'll take Betty, Wally takes Doris and that leaves Phil here with young Sue."

Dennis rubbed his hands and smiled happily, as might a general who sees a great battle plan come together.

After second-house was over, and our film had been stripped, we joined the three girls. I was surprised to see they had brought their bikes with them; they must have left them in Waterworth's yard during the show. Walking along with the girls, we chatted of this-and-that until we came to Buchanan road, with it's dark sequestered jigger. Wally and Dennis whispered something to the older girls. They nodded, and prepared to follow the boys up the makeshift lover's lane. Then a thought struck them: "What about the bikes? We can't leave them. They'll be nicked!"

"Don't worry," said Dennis without a moments consideration, "Phil will look after them won't you Phil?"

While I nodded in some relief, the four of them disappeared up the alleyway. Sue and I were left together with three bicycles.

"Watch me." said Sue, after a few moments of awkward silence, "Bet you can't do this ..."

She rode up and down on her bike 'hands off' then stood on the pedals, then sat on the handlebars, then rode it as a monocycle. Meanwhile, I stood on-guard over the other two bikes, greatly ashamed that I couldn't ride a bike at all. After a while the others reappeared all giggles and furtively adjusting shirts and blouses. "Well," said Dennis jovially "and how did you get on young Phil?"

"Just fine," I replied eagerly "Sue was showing me how easy it is to do it in almost any position."

"Really!" said Dennis taken aback for some reason, "Well it just goes to show ..."

He seemed quite surprised, looking at Sue and I in some astonishment.

What with the promenade episode, and the Waterworth girls, I had arrived home very late two successive nights. Mum began to worry about my moral welfare again. When, on the following night, I still had not arrived home by one-in-the-morning, she made my poor father get out of bed, dress and schlep down to the cinema, with strict instructions to drag me home from whatever wild orgy I might be involved in.

Dad arrived at the darkened cinema and pounded on the side door. He thought he could hear a hissing-bubbling sound; perhaps the sound of champagne being drunk from the usherettes shoes. When he was finally admitted, a scene straight from Macbeth met his astonished old eyes. There, resting across several rows of seats, was a great bubbling vat of soapsuds. Great choking clouds of dust hung everywhere.

The simple fact was that the 'tabs' were almost falling off the stage with the accumulated dirt of the past ten years or so. Rather than pay to have them professionally cleaned, Mr. Clapshaw had dragooned us all into helping him pull down the great heavy curtains after the show, bang the dust out of them, wash them in hot soapy water then hang them up again to dry, in time for next day's performance.

My father took in the scene and, for once, asserted himself:

"Come home at once Philly" he commanded "Mr. Clapshaw has no right to keep you, a boy of sixteen, working so late!"

"Alright," said Mr. Clapshaw brusquely "but be sure he gets here prompt at Ten O'Clock tomorrow morning. There's a lot more work to do before we open Mr. Rosen."

I have sometimes thought that, if The Factories Act inspectors had ever got around to taking a look at at the Kings Picture House, Mr. Clapshaw and the owners would hardly have been released from penal servitude to this day!

Reel Seven

Friday and Saturday:

"Double Indemnity"

also

"Three Stooges' comedy"

Mr. Hyman Bloom was a bustling, energetic little businessman. He had an unfortunate passion for the stage and the visual arts in general. Unfortunate because, in an unguarded moment, his passion led him to purchase three or four old, ailing cinemas around Merseyside, as a cheap lot. He felt, with apparent optimism, that a stable financial basis (backed up by Mr. Gimble's expert accountancy) and some inventiveness and enterprise, one could quickly turn this covey of lame ducks into golden geese. Sadly, this exercise was simply doomed.

The main difficulty, facing any small privately-owned chain of cinemas, was how to persuade the public to patronise. In our case, when programmes consisted of second-rate, poor-quality films of not inconsiderable vintage, people were paying a few coppers more to see better, newer films at the local Gaumont or Odeon.

The Kings Picture house was, needless to say, the lamest duck in Mr. Bloom's brood. It simply could not be made into a profitable enterprise. The programme was changed five-times per-week ... if you can't show a few good films, show the greatest possible variety of lousy ones! The staff worked sixty-five hours a week or more, for pitifully low wages.

The winter heating turned down to save on gas bills, sales of ice cream were boosted in summer by turning off the ventilation. But it was no use; even Mr. Clapshaw's jar of dried peas had little effect.

At this point, perhaps the more patient reader is entitled to an explanation about those peas:

The jar stood each night beside Julia the cashier and patrons were invited to guess the number of peas in the jar. The lucky winner was one who gave the nearest correct answer, receiving a small gift and two free tickets for the next performance.

I began to sense all was far from well and that the cinema might even have to close down. I think our concern was almost as much for Mr. Clapshaw our manager as it was ourselves. I could go back to sieving mice droppings out of the lentil bags in Maypole's stores, the usherettes could go back to their husbands; but Mr. Clapshaw would clearly suffer a shattering personal bereavement in losing his cinema. He spent most of his waking days in it. The 'Kings' had become a sort of obsession with him.

Mr. Bloom and the faithful Gimble began to pay ever more frequent visits. Mr. Gimble's groans of dismay, as he looked through our audience figures, were audible to us up in the distant operating box. Back in his Liverpool office, Gimble got into the habit of automatically reaching for his bottle of red ink whenever he came to balance our accounts.

When, at last, one morning Bloom and Gimble arrived and called a meeting of all staff. So, had it come at last? We trooped sorrowfully down into the auditorium and sat in the front row of the stalls. Mr. Bloom mounted the little stage to address us ...

I felt sorry at the prospect of leaving the place. There was something insidious about the job that got you after a while. It was hard, dirty work and tedious at times, but it sure got into your blood, the show business bug!

... It was difficult to concentrate on what Mr. Bloom was saying. I found myself trying to recollect how many coupons one had to snip out of ration books for a packet of strawberry jelly, and whether you were more likely to find mice droppings in lentils or pearl barley.

"... and so," Mr. Bloom went on "we cannot continue in this way, it is impossible! The films are so old that that no one wants to see them, and the big distributors won't give us any newer ones ... even if we could afford to pay for them ... because that might affect the takings at their own cinemas. So, we are in serious trouble. But, just suppose, just suppose we could get regular supplies of films of the highest quality, films that no other cinema is showing within one-hundred miles of us ... then we would be back in business again!"
Mr. Bloom paused theatrically while we all sat up and began to take notice. Had the wily little man found a way out of our troubles after all?

"In France, Italy, Sweden, Russia, ..., even they make wonderful films, great films, fantastic films that no one in this country has any chance of seeing outside London's West End. Well, we are going to show those films right here!"

Mr. Bloom waved his hands excitedly and his bald head glistened.

"We shall be the only cinema, in the whole of the North of England, showing foreign films. People will flock here from miles around. Ours will be the most exclusive, de-luxe cinema on Merseyside. There'll be Daimlers and Rolls Royce motorcars parked in the side streets ..."

"Mr. Bloom!" broke in Janet "How will people round here understand these wonderful films, if they're all in foreign languages like you said?"

"The words will appear in English on the bottom of the screen. I believe they are called subtitles." replied Mr. Bloom with a beaming smile for Janet.

"Of course ..." went on Mr. Bloom hurriedly, as a thought appeared to strike him "... this doesn't mean you can expect an easier job or more money ..."

The very idea seemed to bring fresh perspiration to his brow!

"... all it means is that your jobs will be secure. But that alone is, of course, important in these days of rising unemployment."

We learned that a lot of money was to be spent to contrive a new image:

More comfortable seating and plush carpets throughout. The facade was to be redecorated for the first time in living memory and, most important for us operators, a complete new projection system. Bank loans were probably a lot easier to come by in those days; just as well, since the whole scheme would probably cost more than Bloom had paid for the whole dump in the first place.

Belinda wanted to know whether the high-class clientele, Mr. Bloom hoped for, would still want their choc-ices in the interval. Mr. Bloom was shocked ...

"Certainly not, that would be quite out of character! No, we will serve our new patrons hot coffee and assorted biscuits instead. Much more in-keeping with our new image!"

"Don't seem like the old 'Kings' somehow." muttered Ernie, the old doorman, with a sigh.

Mr. Bloom pounced on the remark, which gave him the cue he had been waiting for ...

"You are quite right my friend. It won't be the Kings any more; no, six months from now it will be re-named the 'Continental cinema' and a new era will have begun for us all."

With a theatrical wave of his hand, Mr. Bloom leapt nimbly down from the stage and stalked off as if to an exit line. Very fond of the legitimate stage was our Hymie.

As the last months of the old Kings cinema drew to a close, work went on as usual. Dennis Mills left for his new appointment as Chief at the Garston cinema, and we threw a little farewell party in his honour after the show on his last night.

Belinda burst into tears and we all consumed great quantities of fish and chips, washed down with cream soda, followed by plenty of custard pies and sticky buns.

By now I was tolerably proficient in all aspects of the job. I could safely be trusted with the post of second op. Wally, a really bright and nimble-witted lad, took to the position of Chief like a duck to water. Naturally, this left the post of junior operator vacant. I looked forward to us having someone new, who would be saddled with with the fouler tasks; those which had fallen to me until before now.

I was in for a rude awakening ... on the morning following Dennis' departure, little Leonard joined us (we never learned his other name and we didn't much care). He was the only son of a relation of Clapshaw's sister Lucy, and he was to be taught the business. He was small and delicate with curly hair. Wide, innocent blue eyes ... you almost threw up just looking at him. He was considered too delicate for any of the very heavy tasks; those which, to my huge disgust, I was to be cursed by. He had to be let-off early at night, in case the damp air affected his chest! His mother actually called for him most nights, to escort him home. Luckily for the lad's safety, for Wally and I were rapidly being driven to contemplate some desperate act of violence, Leonard's Mother soon decided that the long hours were making her little lad look rather pale. So, she took him away.

In his place a few days later - Ron Summers, an immensely likable lad, who was only a few months younger than I. He had a good-humoured freckled face, and an inexhaustible fund of Scouse wit for every occasion. He was also cheeky and irrepressible, scarcely accepting any form of discipline without a long argument.
A complete contrast to me; in the first few weeks of my job, at any rate, I could almost have cheerfully sawn my left leg if ordered to do so by Dennis.

The three of us settled down to work together, squabbling constantly, and even had the occasional friendly punch-up. However, we became very good friends and went around together whenever we had time off.

On Ron's birthday, we took the ferry over to Liverpool pier head, followed by a bone-rattling trip on the old overhead railway (known as the dockers umbrella), along the docks to Garston. Dennis received us in-state in his private office next to the operating box. While impressed by the comparative grandeur of his situation, I thought his joviality a bit forced. He wasn't the same old Dennis any more. The extra responsibility, and the absence of his old friends, was definitely dampening his exuberance.

At last it was time for the summer holidays. We each had an allowance of one week off with pay, and took our weeks consecutively to share in the peak holiday season. It seemed customary to save up your normal days off, while your mates were off on their holidays, and then add them on to your own week off when it came around. In our case, this gave us each an extra two days holiday, on top of our legitimate week off. It also meant that in my case, Wally and Ron had opted to have their holidays first; so I had to work for almost a month without a single day off.

Mum and dad had booked a holiday in a friendly little guest house, in the old-world village of Neston; some thirteen miles down the Wirral peninsula from our home town.

Having no close friends of my own I would naturally go with them.

However, by the time my holiday came around, I was exhausted from the long hours with no time off, and my old opponent, asthma, re-asserted itself. I travelled down with them by the quaint little steam-hauled branch line, from Seacombe.

But I soon became so ill from the high pollen count, that I had to be taken home again. This meant spending my first annual holiday coughing and gasping in bed, inhaling the foul reek of burning herbal powders from saucers. This, apparently, the best remedy for asthma the medical profession had to offer in those days. Going back to work greatly dispirited at losing my annual holiday, I was grimly determined never to participate in such a stupid system of holiday manning again.

About this time, the first signs of that expected metamorphosis of the Kings cinema, into the 'Continental' became apparent. Strange men would appear unexpectedly in odd places wielding slide rules and tape measures. Oddly-shaped crates and packages began to arrive almost daily, in the tiny alleyway beyond the back door. Mr. Clapshaw spent most of his time arguing with distant contractors over the phone, while Mr. Gimble shuttled to-and-fro between the cinema and his office, like a benign yo-yo.

It was around this time that I was first honoured to take charge of a performance myself, on Wally's day off. Until now Mr. Clapshaw had done duty as Chief Op. in Wally's absence. Despite the pending replacement of our old machines, he couldn't bear to stand idle at the projector. So he brought up with him a small paint brush and tin of pink enamel paint. He carefully painted both projectors in this vile colour and, when the painting was complete, Mr. Clapshaw's visits to the operating box became less frequent.

Almost imperceptibly, I found myself, a lad just turned seventeen, with less than eight-months experience, in sole charge of running the 'show' and, though I say it myself, I did it very well too!

At first I found lacing the film through the projector mechanism quite tricky. The blank film (or 'leader') at the start of the new reel had to be threaded down through a series of sprockets, past the 'gate' (where the light from the arc lamp would illuminate the image), and then into the sound head.

Here, a small light bulb would shine onto the passing sound track. The variations in light intensity, caused by the dots and wiggles of the sound track, would be picked up by a sensor. This would translate into amplified electric currents, emerging as sound from giant loudspeakers behind the silver screen.

To allow for the distance between the gate and the sound head, the actual sound was recorded in the film studio exactly fifteen inches further down the film than the corresponding image. For this reason, a projectionist's more exacting job was to ensure the distance of fifteen inches was kept during the lacing-up operation. Failure to do so meant the sound and vision would appear noticeably out of sync. I quickly became adept at lacing up, and could join in Dennis and Wally's competitions - "who could lace up fastest?" If I recall correctly, I think twenty-seconds was our best recorded time.

Of course, I did make the occasional error; but, I suppose, that was probably only to be expected. One time, I was in charge and spotted a faint black line across the bottom of the screen. Striving, as always, for perfection, I twiddled the big wheel which controlled the tilt of the machine; this in order to remedy the problem. But the line became more pronounced.

I twiddled again. The line became much thicker and the picture itself looked distinctly narrower. I became anxious and twiddled the wheel less cautiously. The picture began closing up into a narrow strip before my horrified eyes. One could just see the actors waistcoats and bosoms, but their heads and legs had disappeared. The hoots from the audience reached me faintly through the sound-proof window, and perspiration poured from my brow. There was a pounding on the stairs outside and a panic-stricken Gimble burst into the box.

"What is it? What's happening?" he demanded.

As always, the soul of truth and honesty ...

"I don't know Mr. Gimble." I said, shrugging my shoulders hopelessly.

"I just twiddled the tilt wheel to try to correct the picture, and now, no matter what I do the bloody thing keeps getting worse!"

Mr. Gimble, forcing his agitation under control, let his logical accountant's brain take over.

"It was more or less OK before. Now you've twiddled that wheel and it's gone haywire, for Christ's sake let's twiddle it right back to where it was in the first place!"

It seemed a sensible suggestion. We heaved and hauled on the tilt control until it was more or less back in it's original position. We glanced in trepidation out through the viewing port ... the picture was perfect!

Mr. Gimble squared his shoulders and strutted away, too pleased with himself to give me the good telling off I richly deserved ...

"Any time you want a spot of help with a technical problem, don't hesitate to call me!" were his parting words.

Reel Eight

All this week:

"Ils Etaient Neuf Celibataires"

Plus

"Pathe News"

The great opening night had arrived at last. Wally Tate closed the brand new switch on the wall by the rewind room and, outside on the newly-painted facade, the words 'CONTINENTAL' spluttered into purple neon light for the first time. Ernie the doorman, resplendent in a smart new uniform with white kid gloves, strode up and down the pavement outside the little foyer shepherding taxis, Jaguars, Rovers and even one or two Rolls Royce into the seedy fly-blown streets around the cinema. The patrons began to form an orderly queue outside; a queue of elegant, well-dressed, well-heeled patrons of the arts.

There were also a few younger patrons whose trendy dress and extravagant behaviour proclaimed them as members of the Scouse Bohemian set. The contrast between this audience and the usual crowd of caps, headscarves and dirty old macs was so absorbing that the three of us, craning our necks out of the tiny operating box window, were unaware of Mr. Clapshaw's approach.

As he tapped Wally on the shoulder, we ducked hastily inside and awaited his pleasure.

"Boys," he said softly "I know you will do everything possible to ensure we have a trouble-free performance tonight, without any horse-play or larking about. I have the utmost confidence in you all. I only wish to say this: if we have a single avoidable breakdown tonight I shall not be annoyed or fly off the handle, but I do promise you that I shall return here, after the show is over, with the necessary implements and personally castrate all three of you!" With this dire warning he turned on his heel and disappeared downstairs.

His warnings were unnecessary. We had already double-checked every inch of film until our fingers were grazed into complex, intricate patterns. The signal buzzer sounded once and I left the box to open the tabs for our opening performance. Negotiating our notorious, narrow spiral staircase, I happened upon Mr. Bloom busily stirring an urn, full of steaming coffee. His idea of serving coffee and biscuits during the interval had taken complete hold of him. It was represented to him that there was not a square inch in the whole of the tiny cinema where three hundred cups of coffee and plates of biscuits could be prepared.

In the end, a gas ring and coffee urn were installed in a sort of little niche, about half way up the stairs. Beating the miracle of the loaves and fishes into second place was how the usherettes ever contrived to brew up, set out, serve, collect, wash-up and set-out again their coffee cups and trays, half way up an eighteen inch-wide stone spiral staircase day in and day out.

I passed through the transformed auditorium with it's comfortable new seats, plush carpeting, elegant decor and politely expectant customers.

I opened the tabs and the first Continental programme got under way. At the risk of disappointing the reader, the programme went off like clockwork without a hitch. The new projectors were a great improvement - much quieter for one thing and the new arc lamps, with their automatic adjustment, gave a beautifully clear white light improving the picture quality.

At the end of the show, as patrons streamed into the little foyer and thence into their waiting fleet of posh cars, all were met by another of Mr. Bloom's brainwaves: across the top of the exit doors 'Good Night and Thank You' was spelled out in French, German, Swedish, Italian and of course Hebrew!

It had been a great night. Our jobs, at least, seeming secure again. Mr. Clapshaw looked tired, but hugely pleased as he sat in state in his office studying the figures for our first evenings takings. The office seemed somewhat bigger now that the sack of peas and the drums of flea killer had gone.

The usherettes were not so fortunate ...

On every square inch of available space in their tiny staff room, on the stairs outside, everywhere you looked there were used coffee cups, stacks of plates, saucers and soggy biscuits. I was amazed by how the girls put up with the inconvenience. Bloom didn't even have to hire a washer-up, the girls did it during odd spare moments during the show.

The contrast between the closed-shop militant of later years and the over-submissive employee of the '50s is considerable. By way of example ...

Despite Mr. Bloom's prejudices, the sale of ice creams continued during the summer months, to those low-minded individuals who actually preferred them to a cup of scalding hot coffee. So it was decided we were to have our own freezer to store them in. One evening Clapshaw called up to say we were not to go home straight after the show, as he had a little job for us to do first. The 'little job' only turned out to be the lifting of the newly-arrived chest freezer (which might have weighed-in at about a quarter of a tonne) up the foyer steps, and then up the balcony staircase, to the landing outside the balcony door. The idea of actually paying for a gang of heavies, to bring the freezer in and install it, would not have entered Clapshaw's mind for an instant.

We three operators and Mr. Clapshaw began hauling the giant wooden packing crate up both sets of stairs (not unlike Laurel and Hardy in the famous piano sequence). We were just one step from the crate's final resting place when Ron trod on the tail of Garbo, the resident cat. Garbo had been snoozing on the stairs. His unexpected yell unnerved us, to the extent that the freezer slipped out of our clutches and rolled down the stairs with a tremendous crash. It came to rest neatly on top of Wally's middle finger which it severed at the tip. Garbo went into convulsions and had to be pacified by Mr. Clapshaw.

Clapshaw was very fond of animals. Then to show that, in an emergency such as this, he was prepared to go to any lengths where the welfare of his staff was concerned ... he actually phoned for a taxi to take Wally off to Central Hospital and when it arrived, went off with him to see the offending finger stitched up.

Meanwhile, Ron and I further pacified Garbo with a dish of kipper heads. In an hour or so they were back. Wally, his finger swathed in bandages, had apparently taken it well and had only passed out once or twice with delayed shock. It couldn't be denied that he was still very pale.

We got back to the job in hand and, before we left for home in the early hours of the morning, we had the freezer installed and plugged in ready for its first consignment of vanilla tubs and choc-ices. The idea of suing the company for a lost finger tip, seeking an ex-gratia payment, or even settling for an extra couple of days off to recuperate, would have occurred neither to Wally nor our boss.

Thankfully, installing the freezer was the last in a long series of tough jobs, in which we would be involved during the course of converting the Kings into the Continental. Everything was done late at night or early in the morning, to avoid conflicting with performance times. So, although the whole cinema was virtually ripped apart and re-assembled, we did not close for a single performance.

Even though workmen and staff alike, might have been seen frantically putting the finishing touches to some job or other, right until a few seconds before doors opened to the public, the 'show must go on' motto was a wise one on Bloom's part. We all knew of instances where cinemas had closed for several weeks refurbishment, only for the patrons to simply never return.

The installation of the new projection system was the most complex task of all. As 'God Save the King' signaled the end of the second house performance, a waiting army of technicians descended upon the operating box.

We stayed with them until nearly five in the morning, ripping out the worn-out old equipment and installing the new; which, if not the most expensive available, was still a vast improvement on its predecessor. After snatching a couple of hours sleep, I arrived back at Ten O'Clock the next morning.

As I half expected, I found that Mr. Clapshaw had stayed up all night, his dress suit still immaculate and looking a good deal fresher than I did myself. Testing and adjustment of the new system was completed by 1:30 am, and by 1:45 am we were open for business as usual. They really knew their stuff those installation folk, and we gave them credit for their expertise while wishing we could have had a day to sleep it off (as they could before starting their next job). As I recall, the long hours of extra work we put in for the weeks prior to re-opening did not merit a penny of overtime pay: it was all considered part of the job.

While all this excitement was going on at the new Continental cinema, the fates had apparently called a special meeting - to discuss a nasty brew of punishments, which were to be administered to the Rosen family. Perhaps one of my tailoring ancestors had made a lousy job of making a Sunday tunic for someone, and they had decided to get their own back.

It all started one evening with a rather strange premonition. It was shortly after our gala opening night. I arrived home after the show to find Mum waiting up for me on her own, which was unusual. Dad had felt tired and gone off to bed early. I relaxed with my cup of cocoa in front of the dying kitchen fire. Mum yawned while knitting (since it was not far off midnight), when suddenly we heard a piercing scream coming from Dad upstairs. We leapt to our feet, hearts pounding with nameless terror.

"It's your father!" exclaimed Mum, her face as white as a sheet. We raced upstairs and burst into Dad's bedroom. Dad was sitting up in bed, an anxious puzzled expression of his face. He passed his hand nervously over his forehead.

"Oy!" he said "Have I had a strange nightmare! A wild beast chased me and when I could run no more it began to devour my stomach!" He laughed shakily. We laughed too in the release of tension, and because it was such a ridiculous dream.

Not so ridiculous as all that though. A few days later severe stomach pains began, and a virulent cancer was diagnosed. Father was taken to Tranmere hospital. Four weeks later he died.

In his seventy-odd years, Dad had rather less than his rightful share of beer and skittles. He was the son of a village butcher; one of a large, poor family living in the town of Krakow in Poland. Times were hard, persecution and poverty were always present, and so it was that the younger generation emigrated to England. Coming over first, Dad was the eldest of the children. His job was to earn enough money to get the others over too. So he joined the ranks of the sweated labourers in the clothing factories of Yorkshire. He did well, rising in time to be manager of a small firm in Leeds.

He was soon able to save up enough to start ferrying his brother and sisters over. They quickly settled down, became quite Anglicised and did well and prospered.

Dad, however, was not so lucky. His first wife and two young children all died within the space of a few years. Then he fell out of work. He spoke broken English and could neither read nor write (except in Polish or Hebrew).

He had been so busy working hard to bring his siblings over, that he never had time to educate himself; making it quite hard for him to find work as the depression loomed.

Despite this, Dad was a bouncing ball, nothing could keep him down for long. He moved to Liverpool, setting up as a wholesale tailors' merchant selling buttons, cotton, and rolls of cloth and such. After a long struggle he got back into the black again. He met and married my mother in 1929 and settled down in the fashionable terraced house in Wallasey (cost £750), where I was born two years later.

For a time all went well. Then, as the depression of the 1930s deepened, Dad's business flopped. He was reduced to hawking heavy suitcases of cheap tailor's trimmings around on foot, to sell to his old business rivals.

He then tried his hand at bespoke tailoring, doing astonishingly well at it ... until a series of strokes paralysed his fingers. What a man! I believe if he could have found a way to sew suits and jackets with his teeth, he would have done it! I never knew a man who fought such gallant battle all his life against every misfortune the fates could fling at him. In-spite all his reverses, he retained his cheerfulness and a nicely jovial sense of humour. He had been a good father and his sudden death was a very deep, personal shock to me.

However, the fates still had a few nasties left for those remaining of the Rosen family.

The folk at the Continental were very kind when they heard about Dad's sudden death and funeral. They clubbed together to buy a wreath and Mr. Clapshaw gave me leave for the eight days of obligatory mourning (the 'Shiva'); when the close relatives of the deceased have to keep within doors and sit on low stools as tokens of their grief.

Among the friends and relatives, who came to join us in our daily family prayers, was Sammy Goldberg, an old childhood friend from my evacuee days in Wales. We shook hands and sat side-by-side talking of old times together.

"Where's your brother David?" I asked. Sammy grinned.

"The schlemiel has gone and caught scarlet fever. They've taken him off to Mill Lane fever hospital for observation. Nothing serious of course, but you can't be too careful with scarlet fever; could turn very nasty. Well so long, look after yourself. I'll give your regards to David."

Sammy need not have bothered. A couple of days later, just when the Shiva had ended, and I should have returned to work, when all the relatives had left and the big old house had suddenly gone all quiet and mournful, I took to my bed all feverish and spotty ...

"Hmm yes, definitely scarlet fever." said old Dr. Ap Jenkins, twiddling his old-fashioned pince-nez. "Better get you off to Mill Lane right away. Can't have your poor mother bothered with looking after you in her present state. I'll write them a note stressing the urgency of the case to make sure you get a bed."

A few hours later, I found myself being whisked off in an ambulance.

Poor Mum waved a forlorn goodbye from the front door. She was now left completely alone, wandering listlessly about the big empty house during the day, sitting for twenty-four long, dreary nights by the kitchen fire. Nothing but the whisper of ashes falling into the grate to break the silence, while I worked out my period of quarantine in hospital.

David was recovering nicely in the bed opposite and waved me a cheery "Hello!" as they trundled me in, tucking in the fresh white sheets around me. It seemed that Sammy, although as fit as a fiddle himself, had acted as a most efficient carrier of David's scarlet fever germs and David, quite unnecessarily, apologised profusely for him.

A doctor bustled up with a loaded syringe.

"Ah, there you are sonny, your doctor sent us a note saying how concerned he was to get you into hospital as quickly as possible. You must have been through a really tough time poor chap!"

I hadn't, it was no worse than a bad cold ...

"So we're going to give you a good, big dose of anti-fever serum to make sure you recover quickly."

As an asthmatic since early childhood, I was quite an allergic sort of person. None had thought to test my reaction to the serum before pouring it into me. As it turned out they would probably have done less damage by giving me a syringe full of hydrochloric acid!

As the day staff left, the night nurse came on, retiring to her little office to do whatever night nurses do in their little offices. I lay talking sleepily to David across the dimly lit ward.

I suddenly sat bolt upright in bed and called out to where I had last seen David. My sight had suddenly gone! I was as blind as a bat.

"David, call the nurse for me, there's a good chap, something weird seems to be happening to me."

I then lost consciousness while for several hours a hastily summoned medical crew fought to save my life.

Reel Nine

All this week:

"Le Secret De Mayerling"

also

"Up the Matterhorn (travelogue)"

It was only my second night in hospital and the worst was now over. I lay in bed, my entire body an interesting shade of purple and swollen up like a pillow case. But, apart from a great itchiness, I was no longer in any real discomfort. In the dimly-lit ward the other patients, mostly younger than I, were quietly sleeping. A pretty staff nurse sat by my bed chatting to me about her Irish village home. I think she was a little homesick and welcomed the chance to talk to even a teenager, during the long night-duty hours.

As she talked in her soft Irish brogue, she held one of her shoes in her hand. Every now and then she would break off to hurl the shoe at a passing cockroach. The ward was infested with them. Great big, arrogant, lumbering insects. I suddenly realised I was hungry; I hadn't eaten since leaving home the day before.

"Wait there now while I see what we can do." said the kindly nurse, putting on her shoe and disappearing up the ward. She returned a little later bearing a tray laden with goodies. As I recall there was soup, sausage and mash, and jelly with vanilla ice cream. "I scrounged it all from the nurse's canteen" she explained, as I tucked in voraciously.

By the following day I was returning to the colour and shape expected of a respectable human being. I was able to relax, enjoy the unaccustomed luxury of doing little but eat, sleep and chat to the pretty nurses. They all joined in the local sport of cockroach hunting, while clearly embarrassed by their clanger, at first visiting me several times a day to see if I was getting over that 'nasty serum' okay.

Another visitor was my poor old Mum. Two or three times a week, she would come along, pressing her face against the outside windows. We would mouth and gesture cheerfully to each other for a few minutes, then she would be gone, as visitors were not allowed in the wards of an isolation hospital. I suppose I was far too callow and selfish to give much thought to my mother's lonely existence at this time. I lorded it at the hospital for the statutory four week quarantine period, during which time the staff were very kind.

On returning home I found for a time that, following fathers death, we were desperately poor. There was no life-assurance policy, nor a will even. Worse still, mother was classed as a 'Polish alien' (although a native of Shoreditch and Hackney) and therefore did not qualify for a widows' pension. Dad was rather sentimental about his homeland and never became a fully paid up citizen of merry old England.

So for many months, until the legal formalities were cleared up, we lived a hand-to-mouth existence. We knuckled down to a dreary diet consisting largely of bread and marge, and watered down sago pudding. By bricking up the sides of the hearth, to give the barest sliver of fire, we could keep the chill off and restricted our ration of entertainment to the crackly programmes on our twenty-year-old radio set.

The biggest problem of all was my clothes. I was still a growing lad but there could be no question of new suits for me at this time. Instead, taking up Dad's old wardrobe of 1930s suits; patching, lengthening and taking-in, Mum made a hopeless attempt to fit the clothes to me. I was tall and gangly, whereas Dad had been short and stout. I looked ridiculous in Dad's old suits and jackets, I suppose not unlike an apprentice music hall comedian.

But there was nothing else to wear, so I just had to get on with it, trying to ignore the predictable sniggers and funny looks.

After returning home from the fever hospital, I naturally hoped to get back to work. However, it seemed I was still very run-down from the effects of scarlet fever and, even more so, from the ill-advised shot of serum. This time, Dr. Ap Jenkins sent me off for a couple of weeks to the 'Penny-in-the-Pound' (a convalescence home at Rhos-on-Sea, North Wales). This in the hope that the fresh sea air, food and exercise would speed recovery. In those pre-NHS days, many people paid into insurance funds to provision for convalescence.

In our case, we paid one pence for every £1 of our income (hence the name). This place was a one-time Taffy-toffs country mansion, set on a wooded hillside behind the sea-side resort of Colwyn Bay.

There were plenty of invigorating country walks, and you could paddle in the icy waters of the Irish sea before breakfast. This place did me a power of good however, and I developed an embarrassingly large appetite. To their amusement, the dining staff found it simpler to just place two plates of everything in front of me, and trust that I would not come back for thirds (sometimes I did!).

I shared a small dormitory with five other recuperating invalids:

Two jovial rugby-playing compound fractures, whose sole topic of conversation was sport.

A skinny rat-faced alcoholic who told dirty jokes and kept a contraband half bottle of whiskey in his 'gezunder' (chamber pot).

A sallow ill-tempered young bloke, with one kidney who grumbled endlessly about his various ailments, keeping a suitcase full of medicines under his bed.

A wizened elderly little peptic ulcer man, with weak eyes and sandy hair.

This last one had the nickname "Fiery Ted." We could not understand at first why, although well enough on retiring at night, he would get up next morning looking half dead. Then, one night sleep eluded me for some reason. As I lay awake, but quiet in my dim corner of the dormitory, I saw a shadowy shape flit across the room. The window sash gently raised, and there seemed the muffled thump as if someone dropped to the garden below. I put the light on and woke the others.

Fiery Ted's bed was empty, and a quick search showed that both he and his outdoor clothes were AWOL. We took turns to stay awake and, finally at around five O'Clock in the morning, he clambered back in through the window only to be grabbed by the two compound fractures. Asked to explain himself, Ted was in a pitiable state. His legs shook uncontrollably and his hair and clothing were in wild disarray as though he had crawled clear across the wooded hillside to get back ... he probably had.

"It's this widow I've got in Deganwy" (a nearby village) wheezed Ted hoarsely, in response to our questions. "I'm her fancy man, see. I goes along to see her every few nights to satisfy her needs. She likes strong, virile chaps like me, y'see." Ted coughed and wheezed himself back into his pajamas and fell exhausted into bed.

It turned out that Ted was caught red-handed by a wakeful gardener, as he climbed up into the dormitory window a few nights later. Matron was woken up and, as the truant paraded before her, he was summarily expelled by the next train for Liverpool the following morning.

And Fiery Ted was not our only source of amusement ... there was the Arcadia cinema on the High St. Bedelia Jones, who lived over the transport cafe, offered a twenty percent discount on her customary professional fees for all holders of a penny-in-the-pound card. There were also Major and Mrs. Prendergast, who would came to the home each Friday evening, entertaining inmates with songs at the piano. The retired Major Prendergast was inclined to conduct massed choirs for ENSA in his army days.

Now he sang boring old ballads, such as 'Pale Hands I loved' and 'Road to Mandalay', in a quavery tenor voice.

All this for the delectation of us invalids, while Mrs. P. tinkled away on the piano in accompaniment. He affected the classical stance of the Edwardian tenor - left hand clenched on the snowy white shirt front, right hand holding up the piano and eyes riveted straight ahead; staring at some imaginary aspidistra plant. Invariably closing with 'Bless this house', he and Mrs. P. would bow to our polite applause, while taking leave with sundry wishes for our speedy recovery.

There were some bad eggs among us, I am afraid. On the last occasion they appeared, about ten minutes after the worthy couple had taken their leave, the major came bursting back in again ... purple with rage and indignation:

"Which of you bleedin' bastards let the tyres down on my car?" he roared. "If I catch the ungrateful bugger, I'll punch 'is bloody nose in ... so help me!" He stormed off in great wrath; a lousy artist but a good hearted chap. I hoped that we were thoroughly ashamed of ourselves.

It was after an absence of more than eight weeks, when I finally returned to the operating box at the Continental. I couldn't help feeling guilty at the thought of all the extra work the lads must have had to put in while I was away. True, the work load was easier now we ran each foreign film for a full week. That instead of changing programmes every couple of days, as was the way at the old 'Kings' cinema. On the other hand, our audiences were now much more discriminating (or at least they paid a lot more for admission).

Likewise, our standards of checking and projection had to be kept at an unremittingly high level - it felt a little strange to me at first (the long hours, the heat, the eye strain, ...).

But I quickly settled down into the old routine. After all, there's no business like show business! It felt good to strike the arc lamps with a bang and a fizz, bawl out 'CHANGEOVER' and to send the steel shutters clanging over once again.

However, the scandal scene had shifted a bit in my absence ...

Belinda had reconciled herself to Dennis's absence, and was rumoured to be going out with a well-heeled commercial traveller.

Wally Tate and our other usherette, Janet, seemed to be a lot closer in their relationship than formerly. I was soon to discover how close!

One matinee soon after my return to work, both our third Op. Ron and Mr. Clapshaw were off. So, Wally and I were running the show between us. Once we had got the adverts, shorts and trailers out of the way, and had settled down to the eighty-minute feature film, Wally made some excuse and left the box. There was nothing unusual in this of course and, even when the first changeover time came and Wally had not returned, I was not too alarmed. The new machines were much less temperamental than the old ones, and it was quite possible for one operator to effect a changeover on his own.

However, after an hour of this, Wally had still not returned to relieve me ('relief' was by now the operative word). I had my legs crossed so hard I looked like a twisted stick of barley sugar! I could not imagine where he had got to and could barely account for a faint rhythmical thumping noise, which seemed to be coming from the staff room. The noise ceased and a few moments later, Wally appeared ...

"Where the hell have you been?" I said bouncing up and down with indignation, busting for a pee. "I've been dying to go for a pee ..."

"Calm down old son, calm down" said Wally, looking hugely pleased with himself. "It's a great day for me Phil old son. I've done it for the first time. I've done it, I have, with our Janet ... in the staff room of all places!"

"Done what ?" I asked shortly.

"Jesus wept." groaned Wally "What do you think ... played abide with me on the harmonium?" while making an expressive gesture with his hands that even I could not fail to understand.

"What if someone had gone in and caught you at it?" I asked, amazed at their sheer effrontery.

"We wedged the door shut with the back of a chair." answered Wally grinning still.

"The only problem was the racket we made on the sofa. The damn thing has castors on it and we were all over the show ... like a bumper car at the fairground it was!"

I was afraid that madam Clapshaw, or old Lucy, might have heard the din and gone up to investigate.

"Well why did you have to move at all?" I asked quite seriously "Doesn't it work as well if you just keep still when your doing it?"

To my alarm Wally pulled out a large tuft of his glossy black hair, in his evident exasperation. It seemed that I had said something remarkably stupid, but I had no idea what.

"Reel seven, four minutes to go!" I exclaimed, fleeing for the bog.

That was just the first of a series of similar episodes, when I was left to run the show alone, while the ancient springless sofa careered it's way around the little staff room below. Once I even caught Wally oiling the castors to stop the squeaking. He said he would like to have fitted buffers on its corners as well, but thought the explanations would be too difficult.

Wally and Janet were never caught at it, which goes to prove some folk are luckier than others! I know that if I had been so ill-advised as to attempt a kiss and cuddle with old Lucy, while she was loading her ice cream tray one night, Clapshaw would have loomed up right there beside me ... I'd have been out on my ear, I'm pretty sure.

Anyhow, I remember the first kids playground I ever sneaked into. I was fourteen-years-old and tall for my age. Having just left my wheelchair on the scrap heap at last, I was experimenting in all directions; walking a lot, pretending to play cricket and football ...

even going off on my own for a couple of hours to relish the heady independence of it all! The kids playground looked tempting; all those swings and slides, seesaws and roundabouts. I felt a great urge to sneak in through the little gate to try them all out ... and I did ... the slide a couple of times ... before, that is, I felt a heavy hand on my shoulder ...

"Ere what the devil's a great big ruffian like you doing in a little kids playground? You ought to be ashamed of yourself!" exclaimed the caretaker. "'Op it or I'll call the bobby to yer."

He escorted me firmly to the gate and out I went. For years afterwards I thought of sneaking in again, just to spite him, but I never did.

"Phil, here's Mr. Lightgood, the company architect. I've said you would help him do a survey at the Coliseum. So get your coat on and off you go." So Mr. Clapshaw instructed me, one sunny morning a few weeks after my return to work.

Our small company 'Bloom Cinema Enterprises' had recently acquired the burnt-out shell of the Coliseum cinema in Wallasey village. Bloom intended to erect a modern de-luxe cinema on the site and had hired Mr. Lightgood as architect (a man well known for his designs of shops and restaurants but with little experience of cinemas).

While we visited the ruins, I held the tape measure and noted down figures for Mr. Lightgood. It was rather eerie in a way. Everything was just as it was on the day the fire had raged through, destroying everything in it's path. The shellac 78 rpm records played at the last performance were still laying, charred and distorted, on the non-sync. A heap of records lay nearby, twisted into indescribable shapes by the intense heat. Cups, saucers and teaspoons lay scattered around from the operators last tea break. Mr. Lightgood asked me many questions about the practical side of the operator's work, with reference to his plans for the new cinema. I answered to the best of my knowledge.

"Now, about the question of access to the projection room, Philip ..." went on Mr. Lightgood, in his thirst for knowledge "... I know there are all sorts of rules about fire protection and so on."

"You could certainly take a lesson from our place, the Continental." I put in with feeling. "The steps up to the box are dreadfully steep and narrow. I sometimes think even a ladder would easier."

I spoke facetiously but Mr Lightgood, who didn't seem to have taken this in as a joke, just carried on taking his notes.

Many months later the newly arisen, aptly named 'Phoenix' cinema sat on the site of the old Coliseum. The projectionists walked round and round the building in perplexity, on their first visit ...

"Where the devil are the stairs up to the box?" asked someone almost immediately.

"Ah," said Mr. Lightgood, arriving on the scene with a bundle of plans under his arm, "you go up there lads, that's the way to your box."

While Lightgood pointed to a flimsy iron ladder neatly fixed to the outside wall of the building, I melted from the scene unobtrusively.

Topically, the eventual completion of the Phoenix cinema afforded the means for the next upward step in my career. Wally Tate had proved his competence as an operator, and the obvious candidate for promotion to chief at the prestigious new cinema.

To his huge delight, he was given the post ... and to my equal delight, I moved up into his shoes as Chief Op!

Eighteen years old, and after only eighteen months experience!

In the fullness of time, Wally was to leave us for the Phoenix. We threw a little farewell party after the show in Wally's honour. Janet burst into tears while we all stuffed our faces with fish and chips, washed down with cream soda, custard pies and sticky buns.

And so, the next day I arrived at the Continental for my first day as Chief! I proudly sported a new cloth cap, which Mum had bought for me in honour of the occasion. At last things were beginning to look up! I had evidently proven my competence as an operator, even to such a stern critic as Mr. Clapshaw. Now I would be in charge of running the show, with a new salary of £3 per week. At last I could begin to make a small dent in our poverty ... life couldn't be all that bad after all!

Reel Ten

All this week:

"Le Idiot"

also

"Steps of the Ballet"

Alfie Beaton was our new junior operator. He came in response to the little 'sit vac' card I had tucked into the corner of our display board. He was promptly engaged by Mr. Clapshaw at a salary of twenty-five shillings per-week. From this you will see that, compared with my own starting salary of eighteen-months earlier, today's all too common economic demons (that is 'inflation') were at work by this time already in history.

Technically I was, though I say it myself, quite competent. As a disciplinarian, you might say I was just a shade lacking. Hardly surprising, given my cloistered upbringing. I found it quite difficult to exert any sort of authority over my little staff; comprising cheeky, rebellious Ron Summers and Alfie the new junior. Dennis Mills or Wally Tate would stand no nonsense. But, I was too young and inexperienced in life to cope with those who should have done as they were told but just wouldn't!

Alfie was a large and good-natured, but extremely clumsy youth. While he tried hard, the poor lad was astonishingly accident-prone. Ron Summers, and I found we had to keep a close watch on his every move. Quite wearing, but very necessary for our peace of mind. Shamefully though, we got our own back on the poor lad by playing practical jokes on him to relieve our feelings.

For instance, one of our duties in the mornings was to answer the phone and take down details of bookings (we had numbered seats like a theatre by this time). Julia Clapshaw would take over this when she arrived in the afternoon. We would sit Alfie down by the phone in the pay box, then slip furtively off to the extension phone in Clapshaw's office. Poor Alfie never cottoned on to the spate of nonsensical phone bookings he received in a variety of faux foreign accents. Regardless, he would record them all in his laborious copper-plate script for Julia's later mystification.

We finally overstepped the mark when we had Alfie record the phoned-in request from a film-loving sheik. He who wanted to book seats for himself and his sixty-seven concubines; all to be landed by a Royal helicopter in the jigger behind the gents bog (with a give-away, remarkable instance of Eastern familiarity with our local dialect). Lace curtains were also requested to screen off his beautiful harem from the gaze of the common cinema goer. Julia Clapshaw, normally quite a prim and lady-like person, came storming out of the office that afternoon in a tearing rage. She had been caught before by the bogus phone messages but this was beyond a joke.

"If I catch you lads mucking about with the phone bookings again, you'll be for it I can tell you!"

We were a rotten lot teasing our Junior Op. as we did but soon afterwards, quite unwittingly Alfie got his own back.

Our new arc lamps ran off AC while the old ones we had recently scrapped ran, as was more usual, on DC. The direct current was provided by a strange looking monster, not unlike a malevolent glass octopus in a wire cage.

It's official title was 'mercury arc rectifier'. There was a high vacuum inside the large glass bulb, with it's array of tentacles, and a small pool of mercury in the bottom which fizzed and bubbled when it was doing it's stuff, converting our mains AC supply into DC for the arc lamps. Now the monster was to be sold off; presumably to some other cinema which needed a spare rectifier. We were to move the whole cubicle onto the flat operating box roof and thence lower it very gently down into the street below where a lorry would be waiting to collect it.

Mr. Gimble hoped to get at least a couple of hundred pounds for it, if it could be transported to it's destination intact.

With much heaving and groaning, we got the wretched thing out on to the roof and then began the delicate task of lowering it down on a block and tackle. Alfie held the guide rope to steady the cumbrous beast in it's descent. The inevitable happened: Alfie tripped over the rope, let go and the cubicle hit the brick wall with a sickening crunch. Luckily Clapshaw was in his office while all this was going on. When we got the thing to the ground, we stood around half-afraid to open the cubicle doors, we were fearful over what we should find.

Then we heard it-a horrible 'drip,drip' noise. It was bleeding! We wrenched the covers off and found the octopus had lost one of it's lower tentacles, hence also it's vacuum. The mercury was splashing onto the ground in great heavy drops. The whole contraption was now barely worth a couple of quid.

We looked at each other in blank dismay. Then Ron, never at a loss for long, took things in-hand. He carefully fitted the end of the broken tentacle back in place, holding it in position by it's rat's nest of trailing wires. He gathered up the spilt mercury in an old tin can and handed it to Alfie to look after, then carefully replaced the cover. If we could only get it onto the dealers lorry in one piece, we could swear afterwards that the damage must have been due to a bad jolt on the journey. Ron's reasoning was sound, but it had a fatal flaw - it was formulated without consideration to young Alfie!

We reported back to Clapshaw that the job had been completed. The manager, busy with his accounts merely nodded without looking up. Just as we were about to take a relieved departure, that prize idiot Alfie burst excitedly into the office flourishing the tin of mercury and grinning like a fool:

"I've just had a great idea Mr. Clapshaw. We could use all the spilled mercury to make a thermometer for measuring the temperature in the hall ... so it wouldn't be wasted after all."

"What spilled mercury?" Yelled Mr. Clapshaw, starting to his feet.

We fled.

I must admit that at times, Clapshaw had much to put up with from his projection staff. Some weeks after the bleeding octopus incident, we were instructed to make up and run through a film which had just arrived by film transport service. It was unusual for us to give a film a test run in this way before public showing. We assumed there was some doubt as to the film's soundtrack or the like. It was a rather turgid French romance, full of close up lingering embraces, passionate utterances and heavy breathing. Ron and I ran it through with bored indifference, until we both sprang to the viewing ports in pop-eyed amazement.

The lover, after pleading his cause in vain with the voluptuous heroine, suddenly grabbed hold of her clothing and, with one fierce yank and a "sacre Bleu", left her stripped stark naked ... all in full view of the camera for a good three-quarters of a second. Her charms were of an ample nature and we thought it best to run the sequence through several times - just to make sure the sound track was okay at this point.

Then, in an instant, the same thought occurred to us both simultaneously (we had kept young Alfie out of the way, in-case he became over excited by sight of such adult material).

Why not cut out the short length of film, separate the dozen or so frames, mount them properly and flog them to some of the lads for say five bob (25p) a time.

This was back in the days before girlie magazines could be bought on any corner news stand, so the market should be there to net us a few quid.

We spent the next half-an-hour or so snipping out and mounting the little celluloid squares. Congratulating ourselves on our shrewd business acumen, when to our astonishment, Clapshaw, Gimble and Bloom materialised in the re-wind room, right there behind us!

"Boys," said Clapshaw in an impressive tone, "you probably don't realise it but that film you have on the rewind machine is of historic importance. It includes the first frontal nude scene ever to appear on a British screen. We may have trouble with the board of film censors of course. That is why Mr. Bloom and the entire board have come over this morning for a preview, as part of their official duties of course!"

Ron was busy sweeping some little bits of cardboard into the waste bin while I searched desperately for inspiration.

"You don't have to worry about the censors at all Mr. Clapshaw" I said at last "I'm afraid we've just had a rather unfortunate accident and spilled a bottle of cement over the film. The bit you mentioned has been ruined, I am sorry to say. We had to cut it out and re-splice."

There was a groan of disappointment from the rest of the Board, who had followed up behind (to see how the other half lived, I suppose). Clapshaw was, quite justifiably, angry.

"You have made me look a complete fool Philip. I am not even sure if I believe your cock-and-bull story about the cement; I certainly can't smell any."

Bloom, Gimble and Clapshaw gave us a parting glare as they shepherded the disconsolate Board back downstairs to their waiting cars.

After a few moments silence, Ron came over and patted my shoulder.

"Never mind Phil. Serves 'em right for being a parcel of dirty old men. Here you are, I've saved one for each of us."

He passed me one of the tiny celluloid squares. I slipped it into my diary.

"You're right Ron." I said after a moments reflection "Dirty old men, the lot of them."

Comparing our lot with that of projectionists in other cinemas, one thing we lacked that they didn't was a staff room to relax in between shifts. We were bemoaning this shortcoming one night, while sitting wedged into a corner of the rewind room, when young Alfie piped up with:

"What about the old prison cells down below? I'll bet we could do one up and use it as a staff room."

That night after the show, we sneaked down and wrenched off the rusty padlock on the gates to the cells. It was probably a good forty years since anyone had been down there. Dark and very dusty, the stone corridor was lined either side with prison cells. Behind the iron bars were wooden bunks, and even a half decayed mattress in one of them. We flashed our torches on the walls to see prisoners' initials, along with the odd bit of rude text or complaint scrawled on the brickwork.

It had only been used as a bridewell, where petty thieves or drunks were kept overnight before trial next day in the courtroom above. But there was an uncomfortable, eerie feel to the place that I did not like at all. After some further exploration, Alfie came across a better option: the old prison warder's office.

It had a table and chairs, a cracked mirror on the wall, and an electric light (which actually worked when switched on). The very place we agreed. Just a lick of paint on the bare walls and it would do just fine.

Next night we started work on the restoration job. We had taken a hammer and chisel with us to demolish some unwanted wooden partitions, so we were hammering away lustily. By midnight we had the job completed and were taking a break, while we took a nip of coffee and a jam buttie. To my horror, I distinctly heard whispering outside in the corridor. My flesh crawled with goose pimples, at the thought of the spirit of some long-departed brutal murderer sauntering up and down outside. We steeled ourselves for whatever lay in wait and tiptoed out into the inky-black corridor. Simultaneously, three powerful torch beams homed in on us, and with a gruff shout of "gotcha!" three burly police officers loomed into view.

Our garbled account, of making a staff room down in the bowels of the cinema, didn't even convince me. It made no impression whatsoever on the police sergeant. The ever-resourceful Ron took over "See here officer," he said "our boss Mr. Clapshaw lives just around the corner, at number five Buchanan Road. He'll identify us. Why don't one of you go and fetch him?"

The sergeant scratched his helmet doubtfully "Alright then" he said at last "I'll go. You two stay here and keep an eye on these lads. I don't trust 'em. I reckon they are up to no good."

The officer returned some half-an-hour later, accompanied by a shivering Mr. Clapshaw clad in thin pajamas and dressing gown. Explanations followed. The boss was understandably annoyed.

The cells were re-padlocked and it was several days before Mr. Clapshaw could bring himself to address any of us directly.

As far as I know, the warders room remained for many years, just as we left it, complete with half drunk coffee cups and mouldering jam butties.

In the weeks that followed this episode, even if we had such a luxury, a staffroom would have been rather superfluous. First Ron went off sick, then Mr. Clapshaw was called away on business. That left just me and young scatterbrain Alfie to do the thousand-and-one tasks needed around the cinema.

Alfie quite rightly insisted on taking his day off, which stretched my ingenuity to the limit; whipping around the operating box to work the houselights, the non-sync record player, trim the arc lamps, thread up the machines, perform the changeovers, ..., and so on.

I must have looked like a species of demented ballet dancer doing a four hour stint at 'Coppelia'. The calls of nature presented a special problem, until I remembered that our flat roof overlooked the side jigger (alleyway). I would clamber hastily up the fire escape between reels, lean over the parapet, and utter a quick prayer that no one was passing down below while I was peeing up above! Then a quick slide down the fire escape and back to the projector ...

No sooner had things returned to normal, than we found ourselves pitched into big-time show-business movie-making no less! A location unit from Ealing studios were making the film, eventually titled 'The Magnet.' They had come to shoot sequences at the fun fairs, the sea shore and back streets of nearby New Brighton.

The film unit had hired the services of our cinema to run through each day's filming, after the spools had been processed, so they could check and edit each sequence on the day it was filmed.

Mr. Clapshaw brought the duffle-coated location director up to the box to explain what was wanted. "All I shall want you to do boys," he explained "is to run through each day's filming on your projectors. You will find that the films are 'unmarried' as we say. That's to say, the pictures will be on one reel and run on one of your machines; the sound track will be on a separate reel, and so has to be run on your other machine at the same time. It will be your job to keep the two projectors running at exactly the same speed so that the sound and the action don't get out of step. When we have seen the film and edited it, we send the reels back to our studio; where they 'marry' the pictures and sound track together onto the one reel of film."

... Which sounded fairly straightforward ...

"When do we do all this?" I asked.

"After second-house has finished each night, of course Philip." Mr. Clapshaw replied "The experience will be very useful for all of you."

This was another way of saying that however many extra hours we might have to put in, we should get neither extra pay nor time-off in compensation.

Late that evening the vans of the location unit arrived and we were handed the fruits of the first day's filming, fresh from the portable developing and drying tanks.

We laced up the 'vision' reel on one projector, the sound track reel on the other, and commenced our film show for our small, select audience. It was hopeless! The controls on the projectors were incapable of locking, to give exactly the same speed (so the sound and vision kept getting ludicrously out-of-step).

After a while, the hero and heroine even began to speak with each-other's voices! Ron and I rolled about on the floor in helpless laughter. It was by far the funniest film we had ever seen in our lives.

Not at all amused, Clapshaw announced grimly:

"The director says it's useless. Unless we can keep the two machines in synchronism, he will cancel the contract and go to another cinema!"

Finding a solution was quite the test of our mettle ... but, nevertheless, we did find a solution. I lay on the floor, between the two projectors, with an oily rag in each hand; while Ron monitored the speech and actions, intently through the viewing ports. At his signals, I gripped the flywheel, of either the sound or vision projector, with my oily rag to slow down whichever machine had run too fast. By the end of the viewing session, my wrists ached and both rags were smoking hot from the friction. We kept this up for nearly two hours, each night for a week until, all the location filming was completed.

As the film crew prepared to pack up and leave, Mr. Clapshaw appeared in the box with a very satisfied looking location director. "Boys, you've done a great job!" he said. "Thanks to you, we've got the whole sequence done bang on schedule, and we're very grateful." He pulled out a bulging wallet, while Ron and I held our breath in anticipation. "Clapshaw has told me you boys don't expect anything for all your extra work, but I'd like you to take these as a token of Ealing studio's appreciation for all you have done for us."

He fished out a couple of grubby one pound notes, passed one to each of us and, with a cheery 'goodbye' he was gone.

Mr. Clapshaw evidently disapproved strongly of such uncalled-for generosity to members of his staff. The sudden access of wealth might go to their heads and lead to untold excesses ...

"You are very lucky fellows but you don't really deserve it." he said, as he turned on his heel and followed the movie magnates downstairs.

We watched them depart in speechless indignation. "Ten hours backbreaking overtime work and we 'didn't even deserve it?' As for Ealing studio's, I reckon we should get our own back, by not going to see the ruddy film when it comes out!"

Agreeing with Ron's outburst, I wondered how many thousands of pounds the film company would make when the film was released.

Incidentally, it is perhaps surprising how often we projectionists did go to the 'pictures' on our nights off. Our working hours were so anti-social, that it was difficult to make friends or engage in social activities; so perhaps sitting in a comfortable balcony seat, while watching the show with a connoisseurs eye for the other fellows mistakes, was as good a way to spend an evening off as any other.

My diary for this period shows that I went to the pictures at least once or twice a month, usually taking Mum to give her a break from sitting alone at home every evening. They made some great films in the post war era. Some of them were good enough to last the intervening sixty-odd years, and still be screened today.

One night, things went badly wrong with the show when we had two breaks in the film during a single performance. The fault was entirely mine ... I had previously checked the film and missed two insecure joints. I should certainly have known better. Mr. Clapshaw had every right to be annoyed, and give me a good telling-off in private. Instead however, he chose to deliver a message to me via my second Op., Ron, ordering me to stay behind an hour after the show, and make a couple of dozen joints in scrap films as punishment for my carelessness. Although this 'punishment' was sometimes handed out to junior operators, I though it inexcusable to pass the order onto me, his chief, via a junior staff member.

When the show was over, I went down to face Mr. Clapshaw. Never in my (almost) nineteen years, had I ever stood-up to, or ventured to query, an order from anyone. But this was different ...

"I am sorry about the breaks. I will try my best to make sure it never happens again. But I can't agree to carry out your order. To pass the order on through Ron, my assistant, will make it impossible for me to exercise any discipline in the box."

"If you can't accept my orders you must leave, Philip." said Mr. Clapshaw blandly.

"Right!" I said, fully determined "That suits me, I'll have my cards whenever you are ready."

I doubt whether anyone had ever queried an order of his before and Clapshaw wasn't sure how to handle it. He had overstepped the mark and would not find it easy to replace me.

At last, a few days later he approached me, the toothy smile in full force: "Would Ron and I like to come over to his house for supper that evening, where we could settle the whole silly business."

I did not relish the thought of Ron and I being bracketed together in the invitation, but agreed to go along all the same.

Julia handed round cups of coffee and cheese sandwiches, while Ron sat on the settee looking embarrassed. Clapshaw went on about the need for strict discipline and the value of 'punishment joints' as a salutary way of ensuring against any lapse in efficiency. In view of my previous good record, if I would tender a sincere apology he was prepared to forget the whole thing.

Ron sat quietly during this speech. It wasn't his fault he was present, while his chief was being dressed down in this way. But the stupidity of it stung me into a sullen retort:

"I am sorry Mr. Clapshaw, but I really don't think I have anything to apologise for."

Mr. Clapshaw glared at me tight-lipped, as he tried to figure out how to deal with the situation, without losing face.

Just then he received unexpected help from his spaniel puppy, who came bounding into the room upsetting the plate of sandwiches, and putting his paws into the tea cups. We sorted out the debris while Julia came back with a plate of biscuits and more coffee. The matter was closed!

Perhaps a trivial incident in the context of life as a whole, but something of a milestone in my early career. It did both Clapshaw and myself some good. It taught him that, although he might be fortunate to have a set of willing galley slaves, we were human beings to be treated with tact. It taught me that there was no need to be a worm unless you particularly wanted to be. It also taught me to check my film joints more carefully in future ...

Reel Eleven

All this week:

"Open City"

plus

"The Building of the Bristol Brabazon"

"Cough for me please!"

We stood in a row presenting a vista of spotty faces, knobbly knees and skinny elbows to the examining doctor; who passed along us in his white coat, like a practitioner on the musical bells performing some intricate cantata ... "Cough please, cough please, ..., cough please, ..."

He concluded his recital and, having thus checked us for incipient hernias, passed us on to the next medic. A light was flashed into our eyes and they would peer into each ear for signs of daylight.

This, the eighteen-plus medical for National Service. I was to leave behind the ease and frivolity of civilian life for the sterner stuff of his Majesty's forces.

Actually, so little of this 'ease and frivolity' had come my way so far, that I actually welcomed the chance to do my compulsory eighteen-months National Service. By my reasoning, it could not be any worse than the life I led 'till now, and could well be a lot better. We had a choice of which service to enter, and I had put my name down for the Navy.

I passed the preliminary intelligence test with ease (apparently, back then, you needed some intelligence for the Navy or the RAF but none for the army!).

Now my medical was almost over. I had been passed along like a tin of peas on a conveyer belt, before a panel of medical examiners. There was just one test left ...

"Down on your knees please and when I call 'three' spring smartly to your feet. Right. One, two, three!"

"I'm sorry ..." I said, in some embarrassment as they stood there expectantly "... but I just can't get up at all."

For some reason it is a feat I have never been able to achieve to this day. Two of the doctors kindly helped me to my feet and one of them reached over his desk and stamped 'REJECT' on my papers.

"Don't worry too much son," said the medic handing me my reject form, "if you take good care of yourself, you may well live to reach fifty." Now, as I write these lines, I am in my seventy-ninth year!

"Ah well, so much for life on the ocean waves." I thought sadly, as I made my way back to the Continental cinema.

Mr. Clapshaw was jubilant:

"I'm delighted they wouldn't have you Philip." he said "Now you can settle down and concentrate on furthering your career here with us. You have wonderful prospects. Only eighteen and already a Chief operator. Why there's nothing to prevent you becoming a manager by the time you're my age."

This was all very well, but it was the present I was concerned with; not at all the seemingly unknown future. True, I had only about two years experience as a projectionist. But I was pretty good at my job (that's right mate, if y'don't blow your own trumpet, no other bugger'll do it for you).

I thought a lot about my work and spent a good deal of time working out ways to improve the quality of each performance. I could lace up and check a projector in just eleven seconds. I had worked out an intricate scheme whereby an operator, if forced to work on his own, could perform eight different tasks almost simultaneously. I was solely responsible for over £10,000 worth of equipment (lots and lots of money in those days), had an unruly staff of two and was paid just £3 per week.

Money at home was still so scarce that I often went around looking like a walking scarecrow. My young cousin Barbara, of whom I was particularly fond, arrived about this time on a visit from her home in London. I found that the only way I could take her out to New Brighton fun fair, was to sell off my collection of radio parts I had spent a long time saving up for. With the cash, I took her on the dodgem cars without her suspecting that I had scarcely two half-crowns (25p) to rub together.

Mum's shoes wore out and and there was little she could do about it, except stuff cardboard into the soles and stay indoors when it rained. Later on we began to take in lodgers, to ease the situation, but at this time we were still very poor indeed.

"Mr. Clapshaw ..." I asked one day, diffident as always in the presence of authority. "... do you think it possible that I might have a pay-rise? Even the second operators at some of the other cinemas round here get more than I do, and I have been Chief for several months now."

The manager eyed me incredulously "Philip! It's barely two years since you joined us and you are now earning the same salary as Dennis Mills, and he was older and more experienced than you are. I am surprised at you!"

I was surprised at myself but I repeated my request. "Well," said Mr. Clapshaw doubtfully "I know how difficult things have been for you at home since your father died. I'll have a word with Mr. Bloom but I can't promise anything. With this I had to remain content.

Although I was a conscientious worker, the Continental cinema was just the place where I happened to earn my bread. If the place had burned to the ground I don't suppose I should have shed too many tears, provided I could have been accommodated at one or other of the many other cinemas in the area. Now our manager, Mr. Clapshaw, was very different. No Brahmin priest ever cherished his temple the way Clapshaw cherished his little cinema. It was his life, his entire world. It ran a very close second to his wife Julia in the adoration stakes.

If we worked sixty-five hours a week, Clapshaw often worked at least eighty, and that for a pay packet of probably less than £10 per week: he could have earned a lot more running a fish and chip shop!

For example, a single instance of this dedication ...

One night the central auditorium roof light went 'pop' and plunged the theatre into darkness. It was after the show but Clapshaw couldn't leave it until next morning. He made Dennis, Wally and I (still a junior at that time) stay behind to fix it. We found the lowering mechanism had rusted solid so we couldn't get the wretched thing down. There it swayed some thirty-five feet above our heads in the middle of the ceiling. It seemed quite impossible to reach. I don't suppose Clapshaw was an exceptionally brave or daring man, but he had us fetch a forty-foot, extending ladder.

We set it up vertically in the middle of the stalls and held on to it like grim death, while he actually climbed to the top. He swayed at the top far above our heads for best part of an hour while he detached the heavy light fitting, fixed the faulty lights and replaced the glass fitting again. He was as white as a sheet and drenched in perspiration when he finally came down. Neither Dennis nor Wally, for all their apparent daring, would ever have tackled that job; but Clapshaw, I feel sure, would have hung upside down by his teeth had such a feat of gymnastics been required for the well-being of his beloved cinema.

I think our manager did realise that not only was our pay below the norm for local cinemas, but that we also had less time off. Maybe his hands were tied regarding the salaries, but he did come up with a plan to give us a bit more free time.

We would each have one Sunday off in every four, in addition to our present one day-off per-week. The trouble was that Clapshaw was incapable of just leaving it at that. He had to tie the scheme in with his philosophy of rewards and punishments, as though he were the headmaster of a small but troublesome class of fifth-formers.

"The rule is this boys." said Clapshaw, the toothy smile ever evident "Each of you gets his Sunday off, but only if there has been a clear week with no film breaks, bad change-overs ... or the like. It doesn't matter which of you drops a clanger, it will be the next person who is due to go off who will suffer, losing his Sunday. That's called collective responsibility."

I'm sure Clapshaw believed this was a clever scheme: the staff would be happier with their extra time off and he would hope to get a better quality of performance at the same time. The scheme ran for over four months and I didn't get a single Sunday off the whole time. Whether it was deliberate, or just bad luck, I don't know; but each time I was due my time off, one or other of the lads would drop a minor clanger. It never seemed to happen when it was Ron's or Alfy's turn. I seemed to be the only one to suffer. I fretted over what I felt to be the stupid injustice and let it get me down.

However, my one-week annual holiday was approaching, and I was to stay for a week with an old couple in a bungalow in Gronant, North Wales, where we had lived during the war. This was Mum's idea. The couple, a Mr. Featherstonehough (pronunciation: 'Fanshaw') and his good lady, had retired from service in India and took in the odd paying guest.

They were cheap and Mum couldn't even consider the luxury of a holiday herself. In any case I had never been away from home on my own before, and so must be protected from any excesses of wild conviviality. Hence Mr. and Mrs. 'F' seemed the perfect answer. So, off I set, carrying a small suitcase full of woolly underwear and clutching a couple of painfully saved up pound notes.

They were a quiet, elderly couple. 'Mrs. F' was something in the Gronant Womens' Institute and knitted a profusion of scarves and cardigans for the deserving poor. The major puffed his pipe as he turned over the leaves of his old Indian scrapbook, reminiscing at length about the old days in the Punjab. It certainly wasn't their fault they had to deal with a stroppy teenager. They were nice, kind, gentle people; but they drove me half mad with boredom!

I took to sitting on the railway embankment for hours at a time, sucking mint humbugs and watching the steam locos of the Holyhead expresses thunder by. I probably got my lifelong interest in the railways from this episode alone. Eventually I was rescued by the local policeman, who took me in-hand and carted me off to the village pub for my first taste of Welsh bitter.

Eventually, after thanking my well-meaning hosts, I departed for home via the railway station at Rhyl.

I had heard about Rhyl: a rowdy, bustling trippers resort. My spirits revived as I tramped the five-miles along the coast road to the town. I recalled old Ernie the doorman's parting words:

"Hey-up Young Phil. Rhyl's the place for you. Smashin' Judies all over the place. Why I remember when I were a lad, there was this red-head as I met by the pier pavilion ..."

He had broken off his recollections in a paroxysm of coughing as I broke off in my reverie to look at my watch.

"Good God, I will miss my train."

I broke into a run for the last half-mile ... only to find that, when I pounded into the station, my watch was fast and I had a good half-an-hour to spare.

Finding the waiting room, I sat down to recover my breath. I looked about me casually ... and my eyes nearly popped out of my head!

Old Ernie was right! The Judies were everywhere, one with her skirt up, fixing her stockings; another fixing her Bra. Cor! What a place! A pretty brunette came shimmying over to me ... I held my breath in expectation of ... I don't know what! She spoke in a husky tone of voice "Say Feller, I don't know why you're sitting there, as cool as a cucumber; but if you're not out of that door by the time I count to three, I'll call the station master and have you locked up!"

As I fled, I noticed outside that the porter's trolley (which had previously obscured the word "Ladies") had now been wheeled away.

Old Ernie collared me on my return to work. "Hey up young Phil. How did you get on with the Judies then? Ha, ha. I bet you had a right old time on the sand hills. I remember when I was a lad, there was this blonde who ..."

I pulled his uniform cap savagely down over his eyes and, leaving his muffled protestations behind, headed for the operating box.

On the way up, I was waylaid by Clapshaw. I wondered what was coming ...

Had the lads been doing something exceptionally daft in my absence, or was this to be yet another pep talk?

"I have some good news for you Philip." smiled Mr. Clapshaw. "I put in a good word for you with Mr. Bloom, as I promised, about a rise for you I mean; I'm pleased to say I was successful!"

I stood agog with expectation ...

"In consideration of the fact that only the best is good enough for the Continental cinema, Mr. Bloom is prepared to give you a salary increase that will take you beyond what is usual for an operator of your years, and experience. But we must have your full and absolute co-operation in future no more sulking or insubordination ..."

"How much is this salary increase Mr. Clapshaw?" I put in.

"Three shillings per-week extra, taking your total earnings to three pounds and three shillings." (£3 .15p) said Mr. Clapshaw impressively.

I thanked him and left his office, closing the door gently behind me.

Next afternoon I found myself, along with a numerous respectful congregation in the dimly-lit Methodist church hall. It was not so much that the local populace had become infected with religious mania, as that the church hall had been commandeered by the Ministry of food (for the annual distribution of new ration books). True, the war had been over for more than four years and there was little real shortage of food, or essential clothing any longer. But, the Labour government perhaps had apprehensions as to the wild excesses likely to result (if such commodities as sweets, sugar, marmalade, ..., etc were to become available to all without judicious restraint). I remember we were allowed two-ounces of butter, two-ounces of tea and one whole egg per week, during the war. When the war ended in 1945, even bread and potatoes were put on ration. The whole nonsensical system didn't end until 1954.

I shuffled forwards in the queue, our spent and lifeless ration books in my hand ... when, who should I bump into, but old

Stanley Kitchener Briggs! Stan was a tall cadaverous man, of about fifty, with iron grey hair and a stern no-nonsense expression. He was chief operator at the Embassy cinema in Borough Road near where we lived.

"I've been looking for you." he said "It is Phil isn't it?"

I nodded.

"Our second Op. has just f***ed off and left us so, I'm looking for a replacement. Interested?"

"What's the pay?" I asked.

"Four pounds-five shillings a week."

"And the hours?"

"You'll get six days off per-month."

I thought things over rapidly. It was a pity about the demotion but the extra pay and extra time off were clinchers.

"I'll be round there this evening" I replied.

The Embassy was a large, respectable family cinema, belonging to the small, but well-established, North Western cinema circuit. Mr. Claude O'Brian was it's small, but well-established manager. In fact, when I faced him that evening across his office desk, I realised with a qualm that he might almost have been the twin brother of Mr. Potters of Maypole Grocery stores (Ltd) who sacked me, two-and-a-half years before. The resemblance was uncanny (both small, dapper, bald-headed and humourless). They must certainly have been related I thought.

A few brief questions answered satisfactorily on my part and I was engaged on the spot. I undertook to start my new job in four weeks time, shook hands and left for my evening stint at the Continental.

Mr. Clapshaw took my notice of leaving the firm in a hurt and offended manner. I had flung Mr. Bloom's munificence back in his face and shown disloyalty to the manager who had taught me my profession. I said I was sorry he felt that way, and hoped we could part as friends. We shook hands rather stiffly; and he, with just a very slight flash of the white teeth, wished me well.

Actually, my leaving wasn't a disaster for Clapshaw. He would promote Ron Summers to acting chief at a lower salary than mine and would have just to spend a bit more time in the box until things got sorted out.

Four-weeks later, they threw a little farewell party for me after the show. We consumed great quantities of fish and chips, washed down by cream soda, and the usual sticky buns to follow (well, who did you expect to burst into tears this time? Certainly not old Lucy!).

I couldn't deny that it had been quite an experience working at the Continental, and we certainly had lots of fun at times. I owed a lot to the firm for teaching me my trade.

On the other hand, I had given good value for money. I had put in over seven-thousand, five-hundred hours of work, much of it hard and distasteful; some of it actually dangerous; and lately, much of it carrying considerable responsibility. My gross payment over this two-and-a-half year period was just over £250 (or about three pence per-hour on average).

Now, I must tell you there was one time in particular when Clapshaw really went too far. It all began ...

"'Bzzz. Bzzz' Oh blast! There goes the buzzer for the intermission. The story will have to wait. Come on Ron, tab-lights, start the non sync, signal to close tabs (hope that daft pillock Alfy has got behind there in time), fade out the sound, douse the arc lamp, fade in the non-sync (oh God, not Charlie

Kunz again), open up the spotlight on Belinda with her tray of choc-ices, shut down the projector, bring up the houselights ... gently now. Okay, now we can relax. Phew it's hot! Pass me that bottle of Cream Soda Ron, there's a good chap ...

Intermission

Cornets and choc-ices for sale from our friendly usherettes.

If I have said little about the actual films seen during my career as a projectionist, it's because I have a weak stomach and, even the effort of trying to recall some of those ghastly old epics, is liable to bring on an attack of nausea. I projected around two-thousand or so films, during my six-and-a-half-year cinema career. The vast majority were dreadfully bad! You who are far too-young to remember 'Old Mother Riley', 'Boot Hill Bandits', 'The Eagles Blood' ... and all the rest, count yourself lucky! Some miserable projectionist, such as myself, had the traumatic experience of seeing such horrors not once, but maybe a dozen or more times over.

Mind you, your projectionist is the last person expected to give a fair critique of any film he has shown. Suppose we have on the screen a really moving human drama, full of tragedy, pathos and romance. Unfortunately, there would be many uncalled-for distractions for the projectionist to contend with. For example:

"Me bloomin' piles are playin' up shockin' tonight Charlie." (the projectionist on the other machine).

"Why don't you lay off the ale then you daft pillock, that's what causes it." (Third Op. bringing in the next reel of film for lacing up).

"'Cos I likes my drop of ale that's why. Which do you like best Worthington's or Allsop's? Me, I find Allsop's makes me fart a lot. Mind you, Worthington's sometimes brings me out in heat lumps."

"You're bloody stupid you are. You've got your brains where your ar... Oh, hallo Rosie love. Your torch won't work? Hand it over, let's have a shufty."

"Do you like my new uniform Charlie? My boyfriend says he thinks it's the gear."

Bzzz, Bzzz! From the intercom. "Yes ... yes? Oh the screen's gone all brown! Must be the fog tonight. Okay, we'll have a look at it."

"I'm not standin' here all bloody night. Here's reel five for you." (the third Op. again).

"Bugger off. It's reel four I want. Dead stupid you are sometimes Ted. Blast, I've snapped the carbon rod. Don't stand there gawping at the picture Phil, go and get us another from the cupboard, there's a good lad!"

... and so on ...

There were other distractions too. For one thing, the projectionist usually saw all the odd-numbered reels, or the even-numbered reels, in any one performance but hardly ever the film completely through in one showing.

Then there was the distraction of the roar of the projector by ones' left ear, the constant demands of the spluttering arc lamp and the clang and clatter of the other projectionist preparing his machine for the next reel, and so on.

Again, the projectionist saw the film only as a small shadowy distant image, viewed against the harsh lighting of the operating box, and through a viewing port the size of a large postcard. The sound projected in a most unnatural manner; not from the screen, but from a tinny monitor loudspeaker behind his head.

To further cloud his critical judgement, he may still have had the bruises on his shoulder from carrying the heavy film cases from the railway station, or his fingers may be sliced in a dozen places from checking a copy (which had become frayed and brittle with excessive usage). Your Daily

Telegraph film critic may have remained aloof from all such mundane matters, but a projectionist was only human and his judgement was likely to be prejudiced in all sorts of ways accordingly.

To be fair, not all the many films I saw were rubbish. In fact there were several dozen, at least, which were excellent movies. But, of course, I had to go to see most of these really good films at the big cinemas in the city on my nights off; since the cinemas I worked in could not afford them. The 1950s were a golden age of the best of Hollywood and British movie making. Studios such as M.G.M, Paramount, Warner Bros, Fox, R.K.O. and Ealing Studios, over here, were legendary factories of great entertainment. If I were to nominate the ten best films I ever saw (and still enjoy today) the list would run like this:

The Third man - Orson Wells action thriller.
Marx Brothers' Night at the Opera - anarchic mayhem with the funniest of clowns.
The 39 Steps - the original Alfred Hitchcock version.
The Wizard of Oz - Judy Garland heads the best kids' film ever made.

Top Hat - Fred Astaire and Ginger Rogers' finest ever dance routines.
Henry V - Laurence Olivier heads a magnificent cast in Shakespeare's play on film.
M. Hulot's Holiday - Jaques Tati at his funniest.
Metropolis - science fiction film of the 1920s.
City Lights - the great Charlie Chaplin at his best.
Snow White and the Seven Dwarves - my favourite Disney epic.

Some of these at least, have lasted the course and are still obtainable on DVD today. Of the remaining nearly two-thousand films, to choose the worst would be almost impossible. But I do remember one dreadful Hollywood Western movie, that we all agreed was so horrible that even the fleas left their seats and trooped out half way through the film.

'Bzzz. Bzzz' Whoops, there goes the buzzer again. One last swig of cream soda and we're off ...

Okay, strike up the arc, fade out the houselights, start up Number One Machine, fade out the non-sync, fade out the tab lights. Watch the film leader now ... 6, 5, 4, 3, 2, 1!

That's it. Open the arc light shutter, fade in the sound, open the tabs and away we go for the second half of the show ...

Reel Twelve

All this week:

"The Dude Goes West"

also

"Double Crossbones"

At first I felt a bit like a mouse, emerging from cramped quarters behind the skirting board and into the central arena at the Albert Hall. When compared with the little Continental cinema, the Embassy was not merely a big cinema ... it was vast! Having once been a major theatre, everything about the place was on a grand scale. The auditorium could seat almost one thousand people. There was a veritable rabbit warren of corridors, old dressing rooms, props rooms and scenery stores; not to mention a cavernous back stage and towering flies that would have done credit to most London West-end theatres.

Yes, the old 'Henry Irving' - as it was known in Victorian times, had been a very fine theatre in its day. One could not help but feel that its transformation into a cinema, however respectable and genteel, was a downward social step.

The plaster bust of the great Sir Henry, placed high up on the stuccoed facade, seemed to show that he felt that way too; glaring down in disapproval at the neon lights, the cloth caps and head scarves ... all trooping in for their one-and-sixpence worth of movie magic. But perhaps I malign the great thespian, he might just have been upset at the roof-top pigeons for what they were inclined to drop on his nose!

My old haunt, the Kings/Continental cinema, had started out as the police court and bridewell of the town; but my new workplace had much grander origins. Sir Henry Irving, the

Laurence Olivier of his day, was a great Shakespearian actor (in fact, he was held to be the world's greatest and the first actor in Britain to receive a knighthood). Now, he laid the foundation stone of theatre in 1899, opening a year later with a play performed by a cast of sixty players. As early as 1904, films began to feature in the programs, in addition to theatrical content.

Billed as 'the wonder of the age', these were the first ever cinema films to be seen by the eighty-thousand inhabitants of Wallasey. These early films included 'The Miser's Daughter' and shots of the Russo-Japanese war. Between 1904 and the time of my employment in 1950, the building swapped between being used as a theatre and cinema. One of the owner-managers was Ludwig Blattner, who later invented the earliest tape recorder the 'Blattnerphone'.

Incidentally, the Embassy was the very first 'picture palace' I ever attended. I was just six-years-of-age and, in those remote times, the Embassy was in a transitional stage between variety theatre and cinema.

As I recall, a stage magician held a mystifying dialogue with a fellow magician on the screen. There was a short comedy film, a cartoon and then the high-spot of the entire performance ...

The houselights came up while a young lady came round selling sweets and chocolates from a tray (ice cream still a rarity). Perhaps, it occurred to me later, I could buy such goodies at the corner shop ... and just as well, without the trouble of having to sit through a boring cinema programme ... anyhow, I didn't ever enter the inside of a cinema again, until a teenager.

Well, now the Embassy was to be my workplace for the next four years. My new boss was Mr. Claude O'Brian. He ruled over his large staff with a quiet efficiency and fairness - reassuring after my experiences of Clapshaw's capricious take on management.

O'Brian had started his career as a cinema projectionist, working his way up the ladder to become supervisor of all the cinema's in the North-Western circuit. He was hard-working, with a keen sense of his position. I believe he would have sooner jumped-off New Brighton pier (Homburg hat, brief case and all) than be seen wielding a flea spray or whitewash brush.

Under O'Brian was Chief Op. Stanley Briggs; very much in the ship's captain/chief-engineer sense ... lots of mutual respect and all that, but with just a touch of conscious superiority matched by more than a touch of inverted snobbery. Next in line was Gladys Oldham; the tweed-suited, no-nonsense cashier, who doubled as deputy manager. There were two full-time doormen: old Joe Crampton and his sixty-four year-old junior, Harry.

Both rheumatic veterans of the world-war-one trenches, with endless anecdotes of their high jinx and the 'Mamselles' when back on leave from the front-line.

They had their hands full looking after the central heating, seeing to the fire extinguishers, killing all the fleas, whitening the stair treads, and wiping rude words off the toilet walls. This in addition to their main task of imposing a touch of class to the establishment. In their smart uniforms, they shepherded the queues to the pay-box windows.

There were four stout, cheerful 'Mrs. Mopps.' Arriving early each morning, they were generally already on their way out as I arrived. There were no less than six usherettes, and a right colourless lot they seemed, when compared to the Continental's vivacious Janet and Belinda. They were mostly middle-aged, wearing sensible shoes (with elastic stockings for their varicose veins) and tended to gather; talking in whispers about mysterious Womens' problems. At least my

Mum need have no fears for her innocent son's moral well-being now!

One afternoon, shortly after my arrival, I popped into the usherettes' staffroom to say hello, and to borrow some sugar for our tea break. The girls seemed a bit nervous at my appearance, and I quickly found out why ...

"Philip!" rasped an outraged Mr. O'Brian, who had crept in stealthily behind me.

"I'll have you know that this is a respectable establishment. We allow no carryings-on here! Don't let me catch you in the girls' staffroom again!"

I skulked guiltily back up the corridor, minus my sugar, half-wondering what Mr. O'Brian would have made of Wally Tate and his peripatetic couch. He would almost certainly have wired the castors to an alarm bell in his office!

Just up the corridor from the usherettes staffroom, was the weird little Holophane room. Here, a squat and rather lonely little robot hummed and rattled abstractedly to itself. This while it made complicated colour patterns of its own devising, to illuminate the gorgeous silken drapes and festoons, used to close off the proscenium arch during the interval. Also tucked into the Holophane room were the house light dimmers - giant earthenware pots filled with salt water (into which lead weights were raised or lowered by cables from the operating box on the floor above). Crouch down in that dimly-lit room, amid the clanking machinery and the odd dollop of salt water spray, and you could almost fancy yourself in a 'U' boat about to crash dive! 'Achtung! Take evasive action!' ... clank, rattle, splash ...

The projectionist's suite was palatial compared to my old cramped and claustrophobic quarters. A large airy operating box big enough to hold a dance in! There was a well laid-out rewind room and, best of all, a comfortable staff room which even had a little stove for making tea. If this was a projectionist's Garden of Eden, the serpent was certainly the Chief-Op. Stanley Briggs.

Stanley Briggs had an obsession about orderliness and an insistence on punctilious-observance of a whole battery of rules, all of his own devising. There was a right- and a wrong-way to do everything; from stripping-down a complete projector, to wiping your nose!

A tall and thin man with a craggy methodistical sort of face, topped by sparse grey hair. He was dour and serious, and I don't think I ever heard him stoop so low as to crack a joke. He had once (he confided in me, in a moment of rare confidence) played the banjo, but he had long since put all such frivolities behind him!

The other projectionists were Terrence Maynard, a quiet and very likable lad. About my own age, he ran as joint Second Op.
Then, young Bill Swift - a cheeky and high-spirited youngster of seventeen, who ran as experienced Third Op. We got on well together right from the start.

The projectors, made by BTH (British Thomson Houston), were very different in design to the KALEE machines at the Continental. For one thing, they were quiet and easy to manage. Most of the ear-splitting racket from the projectors of those days was due to the 'intermittent motion'. This was the heart of the projector. A clever device known as a 'Maltese cross' (due to it's shape) transported the film between reels at around twenty-four frames-per-second. As each frame passed the lens, the film was pulled to a screaming halt, for a fraction of a second, before moving on. It was this intermittent motion that made the illusion of moving pictures possible; but also, if not properly sound-proofed, made all the racket!

The operating box included lots of polished brass-work. The gleaming chrome and amplifier valves, great glowing globes (the likes of which Marconi would have felt right at home with) were most impressive! There was one much-appreciated concession to modernity: the tabs were opened and closed automatically merely by pressing a button alongside the projector.

So, no more dashing down to some little cobwebby cellar beneath the stage, cracking your head or shins more often than not, and having to wait until you got back up to the box before you could yell "Ouch!"

I can't deny that for the first few weeks, until I settled in, Stanley's rigid discipline irked me more than a little (especially after having so recently been a chief myself).

On the other hand, the compensations were considerable: three days off a fortnight, no long dreary hours of unpaid overtime, no more disgusting jobs (like flea killing), comfortable working conditions and a pound a week more pay (nearly a thirty-percent increase!). So, I stuck it out and soon got used to Stan's little ways. Mind you, I always felt that despite the Embassy's larger staff of experienced operators, and rigid discipline, the shows we had put on at the Continental had been every bit as good. But then, I have always firmly believed that one bloke with an ounce of initiative is worth ten blokes, who just go strictly by the book!

I had not been all that long in my new job, when in characteristic fashion, I got caught up in my first bit of absurdity ...

It was one day, about half-an-hour before the the matinee was due to start, when Stanley noticed that one of the houselights had gone out. It was way up in the auditorium roof ...

"You'll just have time to winch it down and fit a new lamp before the they open the doors" said Stanley.

At this, Stanley disappeared in the direction of his favourite pub (the aptly-named "Stanley Arms") for his pre-matinee pint of bitter. At least I would not be expected to emulate Clapshaw's heroics, as had been the case at the Continental. Apparently, the winch did at least work here.

"I'll show you how to get into the false-roof." said Terrence. "Follow me so, you'll know the way for next time, okay?"

"Okay." I said dubiously.

The false-roof was just a thin skin of lath and plaster, a couple of feet below roof tiles, and with perhaps a fifty-foot clear-drop down to the stalls below.

As I wormed my way cautiously into the roof space, I inched my way out over the auditorium to where the house-light winches were situated. Terrence crawled along behind me and pointed out the position of the winch I was to operate.

Edging up to it on my stomach, I began to lower the heavy light fitting down. Bill Swift waited far below with a spare bulb at the ready. After a few moments, I felt a light tug on the cable and began to haul up again. The winch was clogged with dirt and it was tough going.

"Hurry-up Phil ..." warned Terrence "... they'll be opening the doors any minute now!"

"I can't hurry up," I said in a strained voice "I think the cable's got snagged or something. I can't budge it any further!"

"Brace yourself against the rafters; one good yank should do it! It's almost right up now." said Terrence.

I heaved for all I was worth, slipped off the narrow rafter and promptly put my foot through the false ceiling.

"Come on back down ..." called Terrence "... don't muck about. We've got the machines to lace up and it's getting late."

"Don't talk daft!" I said in exasperation "How can I come down? I've got my blasted foot stuck clean through the ceiling haven't I!"

"Stop messing about ..." whispered Terrence smothering a laugh, for the coughs and shuffling of feet far below indicated that the audience were now drifting in.

"I'll have to go back down and start up the show ... try and keep still. There'll be hell to pay if some old bugger in the audience gets a cob of plaster on his nut. I'll be back to bail you out as soon as Stan gets back from the pub. Ta-ta for now."

"Hey Terrence, come back!" I called, in a hoarse whisper of alarm ...

But, he had gone.

I settled down with what fortitude I could muster, to await the return of help. It was useless to try to move as I was firmly-wedged, and would likely unload a few chunks of plaster onto the heads of innocent patrons below. Besides, there was a real possibility that I might slip off the narrow beam altogether, project myself in a highly spectacular manner into the lap of someone below.

No, it would be much more sensible to keep still. I amused myself by wondering if any of the audience might chance to glance up at the roof, during an idle moment. If so, what they would make of a size-eight boot at the end of a portion of trouser leg protruding through the ceiling.

Eventually, after what seemed like a lifetime, Terrence and Bill crawled into view. Both were purple with suppressed laughter!

"You should have seen Stan's face when he came back from the pub, and we took him into the stalls to show him your boot stuck through the ceiling!"

Bill tittered: "Must have thought he'd had one-too-many ..."

By holding on tight to the two of them, then easing myself very gently backwards, I was able to extricate myself without dislodging too much plaster. I thankfully crawled out of the roof space, descending in a little cloud of dust and down the stairs to the operating box. I found Stan surprisingly calm and collected. Perhaps the two pints of Best Ale, sloshing around inside his waistcoat, had something to do with it. He let his face crease into a momentary sardonic smile as he said:

"Back in one piece are we Mr. Rosen? If I had my way, you would have stayed there until the show was over. Still, as you're back, you can take-over this machine. I've been running it for the past hour."

It was steamed cod and sago pudding time again that night, and Mum was lecturing me about my prospects ...

"You have a good chance to get on and better yourself at the Embassy." she said, handing me an extra helping of the vile gluey pudding.

"I met Mr. O'Brian this morning outside the fish shop. He told me he was very pleased with your progress, and that you have a good chance of promotion. But only if you watch your step and don't go putting your foot in it ... why are you choking like that Philip? Is there something wrong with the sago pudding?"

Reel Thirteen

All this week:

"So Long at the Fair"

also

"Joe Doakes Comedy"

I first met Terrence two years earlier when he worked as second-op at the fog-bound Marina cinema, close by Seacombe Ferry. I found him a friendly, likable lad and we struck up a lasting friendship. He had a large good-natured face, snub nose and a receding chin in the best House of Windsor tradition. He walked with a with a slight stoop, as though counting the cracks in the paving stones as he went. We were similar in age and, also like me, he had drifted into the cinema profession almost by accident. Although a careful and experienced operator, he had no desire to climb the corporate ladder. He had found his little niche and was quite happy to stay there. A kind, generous chap, he was also incurably naive and romantic - doomed to countless disappointments as he bumbled on through life.

When I joined the staff at the Embassy, Terrence had a normal grown-up girl friend, who he took out to the 'Pictures' on his night-off.

He seemed far more romantically devoted to her than was usual among young fellows of the day. However, after a while, it seemed she tired of him. She made fun of his romantic ideas. She scorned his lowly job, with its poor pay and unsocial hours.

She went off with a well-paid factory hand and Terrence was hurt, suffering a blow to his self-confidence where women were concerned. He didn't ever attempt to procure a steady girlfriend again.

Some months later, a little girl named Estelle was run over by a car in the street where Terrence lived. Her legs set in plaster, she was confined to a wheel chair. Estelle's mother charred for a living and her father was an out-of-work wino. She would have been confined to her house until she could walk again, had it not been for Terrence. Kind-hearted as ever, he offered to push her around in her wheelchair during his time off. Poor Estelle probably had never had so much fuss made of her before. Terrence wheeled her to the park, the fun fair and the local Zoo. He bought her sweets, ice cream and comics, and played the part of fairy god-uncle with evident enjoyment. Then the plasters came off. Estelle could walk again and could go back to school. That should have been the end of that ... but it wasn't.

Terrence found he missed her company so he continued to see her whenever he could. He took her to see her favourite films, and even bought her little presents from time-to-time. Now Estelle began to take advantage of Terrence. It was not so much that she was a spoiled or selfish child, but that she knew the stern realities of poverty. Her miserable home life meant she played Terrence (her sugar daddy, if you will) for all that he was worth. In a couple of years she grew to be a lively teenager, with a growing interest in boys of her own age.

This was perfectly natural of course. But Terrence found it difficult to accept the change in her attitude.

He took to sending her little poems (which I helped compose), sending her boxes of chocolates and cheap bracelets in the hope he would win her favour; now she was (almost) old-enough to be a proper girlfriend. But Estelle had had quite enough of that boring old jerk Terrence, with his old-fashioned ways. Now, I am quite certain that Terrence would have been absolutely horrified at the idea of any wrong-doing where Estelle was concerned. It was all rather sad. Terrence eventually gave up and no doubt Estelle quickly forgot that such a strange friend as Terrence ever existed.

Terrence might have given up women on his own account, but he certainly took a strong interest in the romantic affairs of those around him. He was almost as excited as I was when I got my first girlfriend. That the event was considered of some importance at the time, may be seen by the green and purple border around the relevant pages in my diary. However, in hindsight, the short affair was such a fiasco that my toes turn up in embarrassment when I recall the detail.

Her name ... Miranda Goldberg. She was a pert little brunette, who I came across (unfortunately for her) as she languished at a local Jewish youth club, between having discarded one boyfriend, and before acquiring the next. She evidently thought my display of callow naivety a wonderful piece of play-acting (nobody in real life could really be as dumb as that!), and she agreed to go out with me.

During successive dates she discovered to her unbounded astonishment, that I really wasn't play-acting ... this was the real me! I couldn't dance, I couldn't swim or play tennis; my ideas of stimulating conversation were limited to anecdotes on 'life in the box' ... like the time Alfie had filled the flea spray with whitewash by mistake and made the back row of the stalls look like a Christmas calendar.

"Let's go for walk on the sand hills" she said one day, pulling me down into a hidden part of the dunes.

"Why are we sitting here in this hollow. We can't see the ships from down here!" I requested, frankly puzzled.

"Well, why do YOU THINK we're here? It's because no one can see us!" replied Miranda, clearly irritated about something (I had no idea what).

After a half-hearted attempt at sand castle building, and telling her about my asthma remedies, I gave up and we went home on the bus in silence. Eventually, the whole thing came to a head ... we were sitting on the top deck of the New Brighton ferry boat, on the way to an outing at the fun fair.

"Good God!" she said suddenly, peering at my face intently ...

"Your face ... it's all hairy in patches and covered in pimples."

"I know," I said in some embarrassment "I've got a lot of pimples just now, and I have to shave round them."

"Makes you look like a hairy Yeti." she said rudely "I can't go out with you looking like that!"

"Alright then, don't!" I said indignantly.

When we docked, I got off at one gangway and she at another, and we never met again. I think Terrence was more upset than I was, and appeared quite melancholy at the sudden end to my first affair.

"Make up with her!" he said. But as I had now acquired further pimples and blackheads, not to mention a small boil on the end of my nose; I saw little point.

Despite his eccentricities, Terrence was a stickler for the proprieties. Again, like the rev Charles Lutwidge Dodson, he went through life with his hands figuratively raised in 'maiden Aunt-ish' dismay, at the scandalous behaviour of those about him. A new young usherette, Patricia, joined the staff some months after my arrival. She was seventeen and, apparently so shy and modest that Terrence came over all fatherly; quite protective towards her. He shushed us angrily if we let slip any colourful language in her company. Young Bill, our third-op, fell for her hook-line-and-sinker. A bit shy, he was seemingly unable to make headway against her impregnable maiden modesty. At last, one night after the show, Bill decided to try the effect of some strong-arm tactics.

Risking the wrath of Mr. O'Brian, he lurked in an angle of the staff room corridor. When the usherettes left, he sneaked after young Patty, grabbed her round the waist and kissed her (with an intensity that virtually sent clouds of steam billowing from his shirt collar).

Arriving on the scene, Terrence was horrified. He disentangled Bill, grabbed him by the scruff of the neck and, hurling the passionate projectionist into the nearby holophane room, slammed the door.

"There, there." said Terrence, full of solicitude, handing Patty a pocket hankie to dry her eyes. Patricia sniffed then, in a voice choked with emotion burst out:

"You bloody great twit Terrence. Why did you have to poke your stupid nose in? I've been waiting three weeks for Bill to pluck up enough courage to do that, and you have to come along and cock the whole thing up!"

She aimed a swipe at poor Terrence and flounced off fairly seething with indignation. I led a bemused Terrence away from the scene, unaware that I was the next brand to be saved from the burning by his excessive Mrs. Grundy-like zeal.

Patty left a few weeks later to be replaced by a slightly over-ripe and over-sexed young lady in her mid-forties. Desiree Davies was married, but said that her husband didn't understand her. Once settled-in, she weighed up the available male talent and found it sadly wanting:

Manager O'Brian was outside her league.
Harry and Joe, the two doormen, were too ancient and decrepit.
Stanley Briggs was a noted misogynist.
Terrence was much too straight-laced.
Bill ... too young.

Desiree's fancy therefore, by a process of elimination, fell upon me! She would waylay me in dark corners and fling her arms around me, much to my initial embarrassment. The embarrassment soon wore-off and I began to be flattered by her rather too obvious advances.

Of course, Terrence was aghast at these goings-on between a married woman and myself (half her age) and wagged his finger at me warningly, not unlike a Dutch uncle.

Desiree lived in a flat over a greengrocer's shop in New Brighton. As the year 1950 came to a close, she announced that she was throwing a New Year's Eve party for her friends. All Embassy staff who cared to come along were welcome. As it happened, most of the staff already had family parties to attend. So, in the end, just Terrence, me and a couple of the usherettes presented ourselves at the door of her flat. The show was over on New Years' eve. The husband was, of course, away. Desiree, slightly sloshed already, and wearing a slinky black evening gown, welcomed us ... pressing countless drinks into our hands as the evening progressed.

Now, my capacity for holding strong liquor was, in those days ... there is no other word for it ... pathetic! Within half an hour I was standing, wedged into a safe corner swaying slightly, with an idiotic grin on my face. At five minutes to midnight Desiree shimmied over and stuck a lump of nutty slack in my nerveless palm. She escorted me out through the front door, saying that when the church clock struck midnight, I was to knock at the door. I was to be her tall, dark and handsome 'first footer' (as the custom was in those days).

The dank night air struck me in the face like a fog-bound 'wet nelly' (a local, rather sloshy pastry). I leaned faint and glassy-eyed against the doorpost until the striking of the church clock, followed by the deafening cacophony of ships sirens, whistles and hooters from hundreds of craft on the Mersey.

I reached up, patted the front door feebly and was promptly hauled inside by Desiree, who had been waiting impatiently on the other side. She manhandled me into her bedroom murmuring something about "it being customary to give something rather special to first-footers." She was about to slam the bedroom door shut, when Terrence (my self-appointed guardian angel) burst in, gabbling something about it being 'terribly late and that we must get home, or our mothers would be dreadfully worried' ... we were by now both almost twenty years old.

Terrence yanked me bodily through the front door and, before I fully realised what had happened, we were trudging home at a smart military pace through the cold, starlit January night. Terrence was silent at first, then burst out with "How could you Phil? How could you possibly carry on like that with such a sex-mad tart of a woman?"

"If you hadn't been so ruddy quick bursting in on us ..." I replied with some emotion "we'd have sodding-well found out wouldn't we!"

Reel Fourteen

All this week:

"Massacre River"

also

"Doctor Cyclops"

"Quiet please!" I said "QUIET! SILENCE. Shut up you noisy devils."

I am standing on the stage in front of the cinema screen, bawling my head off to no effect. My job; to try to secure a moderately respectful audience for 'God Save the King' at the end of the kids' Saturday matinee performance. Our manager, Mr. O'Brian was a stickler for the conventions. To him it was an outrage, to see a horde of screaming young patrons charge for the exits. This, while the Monarch's visage smiled benignly amid a forest of union jacks. So, it was my job (we took it in turns ... all except our chief Stanley of course) to try to keep the kids quiet and seated, until the tabs were closed and the house lights went up.

It was a hopeless task. Our entreaties invariably provoked a barrage of chewing gum pellets, balls of screwed up paper and empty ice cream cartons. We took a step ladder with us and, when the house was empty, the tabs were opened again while we would climb up, dislodge all chewing gum from the screen and touch in with little dabs of whitewash where necessary. Then we would clear all the rubbish from the stage, leaving the field clear for the doormen and cleaners, who had the task of clearing away several sacks of litter from the stalls.

Dislodging all the sticky sweets and chewing gum from the seats, we'd then spray the whole auditorium with a few gallons of scented DDT. This last task to kill all the newly-imported fleas and drown the stench of several hundred unwashed, incontinent kiddies. All to be completed in time for first house to open it's doors to the adult public ninety-minutes later!

Our two elderly doormen, Joe and Harry, had a tough time during these matinees. We would see them through the operating box viewing ports striding up and down, their arms flailing wildly and mouths agape in stertorous (but of course to us, silent) shouts of "BE QUIET!"

Every so often, when the going got too rough, the buzzer would sound twice (the signal for us to stop the show and put the house lights up). We would leave things like this until the mob had settled down a bit, then off we'd go again.

Given these circumstances, there was only one way we could hope to get through the advertised programme in time for us to nip home for our tea break ... speed up the projectors!

Luckily, our machines had variable speed control. Later models did not have this useful facility; rather they were locked to the mains supply frequency. Not unlike the omission of starting handles on modern cars, it was a feature sadly missed by those concerned. The greater the number of interruptions, the more the film speed would be wound up until the projectors roared and rattled like old tramcars on their way to the depot. The manly drawl of Hop-along Cassidy would ascend to a Micky Mouse squeak. The heroine's plea to be saved from the dastardly villains, who had stolen the deeds from her Daddy's gold mine, sounded more like a neurotic sparrow chirping for it's breakfast. The kids didn't ever seem to mind the liberties we took with the programme. Perhaps it made the action faster, the comedy funnier and the boring bits shorter ... so who would care?

If the doormen and cleaners loathed the kids matinees, such shows were also no more popular with the projectionists. It involved us making-up and checking a whole extra two-hour programme, as well as the normal Saturday work. After showing, the film had to be stripped off its reels and re-packed for collection by the film transport people early next morning. A typical programme might comprise a Popeye or Micky Mouse cartoon, a two-reel Laurel and Hardy or Three Stooges comedy, a 'horse opera' Western and finally, the all-important serial (such as the epic adventures of Flash Gordon or Batman and Robin). The kids loved them and would troop along week-after-week, clutching their sixpences (2.5 pence in decimal money); jostling on the pavement outside in an unruly cap-hurling, pigtail-pulling throng ... until foyer doors were flung open.

At half-past-four on a saturday afternoon, it was time for me to mount the stage once more and face that sea of rowdy, undisciplined youngsters. I found myself thinking 'was I ever like that as a kid?' Or even 'was I ever a kid at all?' The answer on reflection was categorically 'No' to both rhetorical questions.

My most vivid childhood memory is of my bed, with its heavy carved wooden headboard, tucked into a corner of my parents bedroom. I seemed to spend a weary part of both my waking- and sleeping-life there. My young fingers got to know every swirl and leaf pattern in those carvings (through tracing them over and over again as I lay waiting for my asthma to go away, praying for Dr. Ap Jenkins to break a leg on his way upstairs to visit me).

Dr. Ap Jenkins was our silver-haired, stripe-trousered Welsh family practitioner. He was kindly, full of sympathy and next to bloody useless! I hated him and his great syringe full of adrenaline. I have since gone through later life with a somewhat morbid fear of injections of any kind.

When I was well, I would bring my toys down to the stone-flagged kitchen and watch Mrs. Mount, the char lady, put 'Zebo' on the shiny black kitchen range.

She polished away at the sabbath candlesticks with a rag doused in 'Brasso' while, if the weather was fine, I would be muffled up and stuck on a chair in a sheltered corner of the back yard. From there I had a fine view of the coal shed, the wash-day mangle and the outside loo. I would sit there in solitary state, listening to the kids whooping and yelling in the passageway just behind the high brick backyard wall. I was as marooned from my kind, as much as any Ben Gunn or Edmund Dante were from theirs'.

In 1939 I was eight years-old. My kidneys ground to an abrupt halt. Dr. Ap Jenkins brought in an eminent Rodney St. specialist to assist him in his diagnosis. There were no kidney machines, antibiotics or other wonder drugs in those days. The eminent specialist looked down at me and coughed "Er, give him a glass of orange juice and a Jacobs cream cracker every four hours. That will be five guineas please." He coughed again and left. The prescription appeared inadequate (perhaps the cream crackers were not up to BP standard). In all events, there could be no doubt that after a few days of such treatment, I was sinking fast. While my Aunts and Grandparents arrived from London to see me off, I dutifully sank into a coma.

"We must change his name at once!" said my grandfather decisively. Agreeing, my father and they hurried off to the local synagogue to arrange the formalities ...

The theory behind this old Jewish practice goes something like this:

God says to the angel of death "Right Fred. Nip down below and get young Philip Rosen. His time's up."
Meanwhile Philip's crafty relatives have given him an extra name (it's always the same name in these cases) 'Chaim' meaning 'life'.
The angel of death comes puffing back up to heaven in a nasty mood ... "Can't find him anywhere." he says "All I found was a Chaim Philip Rosen. No good I suppose?"

"No record of that name in my data file" says God slamming his laptop shut.

"'Tell you what, nip over to the canteen and grab yourself a coffee. Then go on to the next name on the list - I think it's Hymie Finkelberg."

"Right 'O" says the angel of death, with excessive familiarity, as he screws up and tosses away the bit of paper with 'Philip Rosen' written on it "So, you win some, you lose some ..." he would supposedly say, shrugging his shoulders indifferently.

The deed was done and then, as my sorrowing relations stood by my bedside, I suddenly sat up. Catching sight of my grandfather (or Zaida), who invariably tipped me some pocket money on his visits, said "Hello Zaida. Where's my shilling?"

By the time I had fully recovered from that little lot, our prime minister Neville Chamberlain and Adolf Hitler were busy throwing umbrellas and peace treaties at one another. When war was declared in September 1939, Dad was too old for war service and shoving me into a cold, damp air raid shelter would hardly have been ideal for my future well-being. So, we shipped ourselves off to a little cottage in North Wales. The owner was glad to let us have the use of it, his peacetime holiday home, for a nominal rent just so he could be sure it would be cared for, vandal-free. It was a cosy little place with a wind-up gramophone, but no kitchen. It had just a bench with a row of Valor paraffin stoves instead. For the next six years, until the war was over, all our meals were cooked on these smelly refugees from a boy scout's camp. In latter years, I could never taste a cooked meal without being faintly surprised at the lack of any flavour of paraffin oil.

Gronant, a village in Wales where we now lived, was a friendly little place. I was still stuck at home through ill-health but at least not as isolated as before. The local kids took to dropping by on their way home from school for a quick chat and a game of snakes and ladders.

I got to know all their names and all the local gossip, even though I was scarcely ever allowed beyond the confines of the little front gate. I could read better than most of the village kids, and was often in demand to read aloud the 'Hotspur' or 'Adventure' to them.

I was, I suppose, a reasonably intelligent young lad and tried every way I knew to widen my little horizon. I lapped-up the daily schools broadcasts on the radio and read every book on the shelves of Mr. Jonas Makin's village subscription library. I took up model making, photography, map making, wood carving and anything else that took my fancy. But radio (the wireless) and all things electrical soon became my overriding passion. The grown-ups in the village soon went out of their way to help me along in this, my chief interest.

Old Dan Walker, a retired one-armed sailor, lived in the cottage opposite. He was an amateur radio enthusiast and had a special adapter on his wooden stump to take an electric soldering iron. I learned my elementary electrical theory from him. Further, some more practical stuff from Tom Strong, a retired electrician at the end of the lane. He had a paddock behind his cottage for the dapple grey ponies he allowed kids to ride on. He would break off from taking the village kids around on his ponies to come over. Most welcome with me, he would show me how to make a morse code buzzer, or a crystal and cat's-whisker wireless set. Even Zebediah Morgan, the taciturn old village plumber, was heard to stump along to our front door one night and drop something large and heavy on the doorstep, before disappearing without a word. When we opened the door we found a veritable treasure chest of vintage radio parts (which would be worth a small fortune today!).

I was, I believe, tolerably happy at this time in my early teens. I had the village children for after-school company, and my many hobbies to pass the weary hours away. But there was no denying the wartime winters were rough. Interminable snow drifts outside and candlelight inside when the power lines came down.

The shouts and laughter of the kids playing outside, would come to me faintly through the tightly shut window (with it's hermetic sealing to guard against enemy poison gas attacks). I would press my face tightly against the steamed up glass; while watching others build snowmen, run sledges up and down the lane and close with a customary, chaotic snow-fight. I was not, of course, allowed outside when their was such a potentially toxic substance as snow about!

I would wave to them and sometimes they would wave back ...

"QUIET! Shut up you young ruffians!" I yell at the kids matinee audience, all in a frenzy of ill-tempered annoyance, as I stamp up and down the stage of the Embassy. The kids yell back twice as loud!

These grubby, high-spirited youngsters, who had trooped in from the back-street slums of Seacombe, might have been born on a different planet for all I had in common with them. They were free to roam the streets, climb trees, paddle in the mud and be chased all-over ad-nauseam for pinching apples and such. They could swim, roller skate, play footy and cricket, give and receive black eyes and bloody noses. They even attended school from time to time! They are familiar with such mysteries as the stinks lab, the swish of the headmasters cane (this, the unenlightened 1950s), sports day and so on. No, I just couldn't relate to these kids at all. Noisy, dirty little horrors, the lot of them!

Now Terrence, my co-second Op, was very tolerant of children. He actually liked them! On Saturday matinees he would dive into the throng, asking the kids which part of the show they liked the best, find lost caps and scarves, and re-unite lost toddlers with their careless elder brothers or sisters. He was a really good guy was Terrence. I was always relieved when, after the disappointment of losing his girl friend, he suddenly became impassioned by a fresh and totally unexpected enthusiasm - to become a tycoon in the retail trade!

"A little sweets and tobacco shop Phil. That's the thing." said Terrence, as he cheerfully whirled the rewind machine one morning.

"I've got just the place, a little shop that's been empty for quite a while. The agent says I can rent it cheap 'cos it's in a difficult area. But he says he thinks I can make a go of it. We'll go down on Sunday morning, clean it up and give it a lick of paint on the outside."

"'Course I won't run it full-time at first, just now and again during my time off. Then, when I make a real go of it, I can leave old Stanley and the box and set up properly in the retail business."

In his enthusiasm, Terrence span the rewind handle too fiercely, snapping the film and sending a great wriggling mass of the stuff high into the air. This act of over-exuberance left inextricable coils about his head and shoulders (I always enjoyed watching this happen to other people!).

"You're bloody daft, you are!" Was old Stanley's comment. "You know as much about running a shop as my arse! Why can't you stick to a proper trade like me?"

Terrence just grinned, as you never got anywhere with old Stan. He had an answer for everything.

Next Sunday morning, Terrence and I trundled a large decrepit wheelbarrow, laden with pots of paint, brushes, ladders and such, down to the scene of his freshest venture into private enterprise. The shop was in a rather nice, old-world part of town, close by the old penny bridge in Poulton. There were rows of neat little stone-faced terraced houses with ivy-covered porches. There was even a little detached cottage dating, as the stone over it's lintel proclaimed, from 1670. The streets were cobbled and it was all rather pleasant and secluded. It was evidently so secluded that the town planners completely missed it off their lists of streets to be demolished, while making way for high-rise flats. Eventually, they did find the place and at once, razed it to the ground, making way for a motorway approach road.

The shop had evidently been a cobbler's place, but the thick layers of dust and musty smell proclaimed it as having laid empty for quite some time. We got to work, cleaned the place up, made some counter space and painted the outside a pleasant shade of bright pink.

"It was the only colour me uncle had to spare." Explained Terrence, apologetically, as he teetered on his step ladder by the front door.

On the following Sunday, down we went for the Grand Opening. The wheelbarrow was this time piled high with glass screw-top jars, filled with toffees, jelly babies, mint humbugs, and other such delicacies.

"They fell off the back of a lorry." said Terrence with a smirk. At the time, I thought of how Terrence must have been very fortunate ... to have been passing by when they fell off, and even more fortunate that the sweet jars had not smashed to smithereens when they fell.

We set the jars up in a row on the counter and opened the door for business. Our first customer was a massive be-aproned battle-axe of a woman. As she came marching in, casting a look of contempt on the jars of jelly babies, and the like, she smashed her ham-like fist on the counter and roared "'Oo's in charge here?"

"Er, I am ..." said Terrence backing away nervously "... why?"

"Why? Why?" the woman roared, purple with indignation "Because I owns the sweet shop round the corner don't I! I've been there, rain or shine, for the past thirty years or more haven't I!"

"And there's no bloody room for two of us. So you pack your piddling jars of jelly babies back on your wheelbarrow, and 'op it before I loses me temper!"

"Er, what if I don't?" said Terrence faintly ...

"I'll go straight round to the 'elth people and tell them you're selling sweets in a premises that 'avn't got no water laid on for washing yer 'ands."

She glowered malignantly and went off slamming the door behind her.

"She's right you know." said Terrence with a sigh. "We haven't got water laid on. I was hoping nobody would find out."

We packed the jars back on the wheelbarrow and trundled off back to Terrence's home, while the little shop with the bright pink fascia and "T MAYNARD SWEETS & TOBACCO" over the door seemed to peer unhappily after us through the rising dockland mist. Perhaps it blamed itself for not having any running water.

"Ah well!" Said Terrence after a while, as we put the heavy barrow down and sat by the kerb to rest. "These things happen. It's just bad luck I suppose."

He unscrewed one of the jars ... "Feel like a jelly baby Phil?"

I nodded. We sat and munched while the mist stealthily rose round us. Soon, thankfully, we hid the barrow with its pile of sticky, unsalable sweet jars from our view.

Reel Fifteen

Monday, Tuesday & Wednesday this week:

"The Desert Hawk"

also

"Tomahawk Trail"

I was in trouble again. Nothing unusual in that perhaps, but painfully stupid all the same ...

Behind the screen, on the gloomy vastness of the Embassy, back-stage were a pair of towers about twenty-feet-high, each with a small wooden platform top. They bore the big trumpet-shaped loudspeakers, which hurled the amplified sound track down into the auditorium. One of these had developed an annoying crackle; probably a loose connection. Against my better judgment, I had gone up to fix it ... but now I couldn't get down! There was a ladder there of course. I had put it there myself, climbed up to the top and, to my excitement, fixed the speaker. Now vertigo took over ... no way could I could force myself to walk backwards onto the top rung of the ladder.

After a while Bill and Terrence came backstage to see what was holding me up. In spite my explanation, neither could understand my (apparently strange) phobia of heights. I tried harder than I had ever in my life to overcome my fear, but it was no use.

My muscles just wouldn't do as I wished and I was stuck; like a reluctant pole-squatter amidst the dust and cobwebs. I had the odd thought that, if I were still there when the performance began, I should probably be blown off the platform by the roar of sound from the speaker!

I owed my eventual release to Sam Mc Fann the Westrex man, who happened to be making one of his routine calls that morning. Coming backstage to inspect the sound system, he was puzzled to see me high up on the platform tightly embracing one of his loudspeaker brackets for dear life.

"What's up laddie?" he called. I told him what was up ...

"Lie doon on yer belly and crawl to the edge. Then put your foot on the top rung of the ladder ... that's the way. Yer dooin' fine!"

I climbed shakily down and thanked Sam most profusely, feeling very foolish all the same.

"That's aw'right laddie ..." he said smiling broadly, unloading an armful of test gear onto the dusty floorboards.
"I used to be awful scared of heights myself, when I was a wee laddie that is. I got over it of course."

I doubted if I should ever 'get over it' as I tried to brush off the thick layer of dust, coating the front of my clothes ...

Now, Sam's job was one I had often envied. He pottered around in his little van covering all the cinemas in the area equipped with the 'Westrex' sound system. His opposite number, the RCA man, covered all the other cinemas; those equipped with the alternative sound system made by the Radio Corporation of America. Sam visited us several times a year (by contract) to check over all the sound equipment, replace old valves and run his little test film through each projector, while checking the fidelity of the sound coming from the loudspeakers.

I was always eager to help him with his test equipment, as he peered at the decibel meters and frequency response gear, which he used to check sound quality against the guaranteed standard his company was paid for.

I thought him a bit like Willy Nilly Postman in Dylan Thomas's Welsh village, picking up bits of gossip at each cinema on his rounds and relaying it with amplification to the others (which operator was having-it-off with which usherette, which manager was known to be fiddling the books, which doorman had been carried-off drunk and insensible, ..., and so on. Our's was (at least for most of the time) a dull and respectable cinema, so it was necessary to supply Sam with ersatz scandal in order to instill some balance. Sam went away satisfied with tales of Mr. O'Brian having taken to smoking pot, to blot out the anguish of his passion for Gladys the cashier, ..., and lots of rubbish of a similar nature. Once sam had gone off on his rounds, it would all come back to us from neighbouring cinemas with even more exotic embellishments.

Sam kept us in touch with some of the latest technical developments. Experiments were being carried out with 3-D movies using coloured spectacles ... Stereophonic sound and wide-screen presentation, ..., were all coming.

Believing exciting times lay ahead, soon we thought that all films would be in 3-D. Perhaps even the senses of smell and touch would be simulated to provide the ultimate in realism. However, such prophecy is notoriously unreliable. Only now, almost sixty-years later, are 3-D films, using polarised light spectacle technology, becoming popular.

While developments we could not have dreamed of then, such as digital automated projection, are now quite commonplace. Who could have imagined that, the half-hundredweight load of heavy steel cases containing the reels of film for an evening's programme, would one day be replaced by a tiny silicon chip less than the size of a postage stamp?

Much more important from our point of view, however, was the gradual introduction of safety film at around this time. Prior to this, operators had to accept the risk of being burned alive by explosively-prone nitro-cellulose film, which was an uncomfortable feeling at the back of one's mind at the time. The new safety film was produced on a harmless acetate base, which merely smouldered reluctantly if ignited. There was certainly no longer any fire risk. True, the acetate film was much harder to join together than the old nitro cellulose stock. One had to use a special tool, which scraped the ends to be joined and applied pressure to the joint. So, the task of making up new programmes now took a good deal longer than before. Still, a small price to pay for removing the risk of sudden and involuntary cremation.

Safety film also had the added bonus of keeping the fire prevention officer away for longer periods. This grim official took his duties very seriously, making a sudden swoop on the box when you least expected it. Out would come the notebook to record the slightest deviation from the fire regulations.

Woe betide you (as it sometimes woe betided me) if he found a fire door propped open for fresh air, loose film laying about or, worse, a fire extinguisher which had lost it's squirt.

This official had the job of ensuring that, so far as was possible, the audience would leave the cinema as raw and uncooked as when they entered. I am happy to say that, despite our occasional carelessness, he was invariably successful.

A much more welcome visitor to our cinema was Brian Coulter, the itinerant electrician. Brian was employed by a contracting firm who specialised in cinema work. So whenever there was a bit of old conduit to replace, or a new fuse board to install, there would be Brian with his tin box of tools slung over his shoulder, his chipped enamel billy can, and a seemingly inexhaustible store of wisecracks and cheeriness. Brian was an unusual chap. He'd had a good grammar school education, but had been forced to give up any hope of university education by the sudden death of his father. So he settled down to a trade instead.

He was exceptionally well-read, a play-goer and classical concert buff, a tolerably good artist and was well-up on the arts more generally. He was tall and lanky, with a streak of unruly hair over his forehead. Aside from work, he affected the hairiest of tweed sports jackets, priding himself on the neatness of his attire; shoes highly polished, tie knotted 'just so'. Brian was an articulate, very forthright speaker at the weekly meetings of the Wallasey Young Conservatives. His harsh, but infectious laugh would echo over the pamphlet-strewn corridors, and the committee rooms of the YCHQ, like a breath of much-needed fresh air (amid all the political gas and hot air).

"Why not join the YCs yourself" suggested Brian, on one of his professional visits. "Come along on your night off. I'll introduce you to the gang. We're a great crowd. You'll enjoy yourself and it will really help with this shyness problem you're always on about."

... I said I would think about it ...

There was no doubt in my mind that the Tories were a much nicer crowd than the Labour lot. Mum and Dad had always been staunch Conservatives, so by a natural process of reaction I ought to have been a red-hot, left-wing Socialist (as were the majority of my friends and workmates). However, there were other factors to consider:

The post-war Labour government of Atlee, Cripps and Bevan was perhaps unjustly blamed by many (including myself) for perpetuating the atmosphere of gloom and austerity; that which lingered well on into the 1950s. As a Jew, I was infuriated at the way foreign policy was biassed against letting Jewish refugees from the Holocaust enter Palestine.

This acted as a litmus paper among Jewish opinion, turning its vote from red to blue at a stroke. The Tories promised an end to rationing and petty controls, and a brighter future for all. Even if one didn't believe all this propaganda, it was a well-known fact that the birds in the Young Conservatives had much bigger tits than their cousins in the Young Socialists.

So, I joined the Young Conservatives about a year after starting my job at the Embassy cinema. I have those staunch followers of Disraeli, Churchill and Anthony Eden to thank for turning me from an uncouth muppet, into some semblance of a normal, articulate social animal. Brian and I had so much in common that, although he was some years older than I, we soon became firm friends. This friendship endured for many years, until long after we were both married.

We would meet each Wednesday night (my regular night off), under the approving gaze of the great W.S Churchill (he hung at a slightly rakish angle from the Derby House committee room wall). We were a mixed bag and remarkably classless:

The chairman (known as 'Fred the egg') pottered around in his little van selling eggs.
There was a Queens' council, an architect, a plumber an electrician, ..., etc. This regular contact with well-educated, tolerant human beings of both sexes, and all classes, worked wonders in developing my personality. I can recommend this course of treatment to any shy, inarticulate young person. It doesn't matter too much what the organisation is for, so long as it's broadly-based and tolerant of human frailty - young Conservatives, young Communists, Flat Earth League, wild goose fanciers ... what you will, provided they are a nice, friendly crowd, that's all that counts.

Over the course of time I even became Vice-Chairman, and a proficient speaker at political meetings. I came to realise there were young folk around even more shy and tongue-tied than me.

"Going to the festival Phil?" asked Brian casually, as we sat one evening at the YCs sorting out election pamphlets. It was 1951, the 100th anniversary of the Great Exhibition in Hyde Park. The government had done something popular, at last, by declaring this to be Festival of Britain year. Now everyone, who was anyone, went down on a pilgrimage to to London's South Bank (where the Royal Festival Hall now stands), to see the great exhibition of the latest in British arts, science and engineering.

"What me go to London? Good Lord!" The audacity of the idea, at first struck me breathless. But then I considered ...

"Why not indeed!"

All Mum's relatives lived in a close-knit family circle in the East-End of London, and any one of them would surely be glad to put me up for a few days. With a bit of effort, I could save enough for a cheap excursion fare to Euston, and the pocket money I would need for sightseeing.

"Okay Brian." I said nonchalantly. "See you down there!"

Brian had already booked his holiday and so was going down first. I would meet him there and together we would paint the town red. That was the plan (but reckoned without Mum's London relatives). The last time they had clapped eyes on me, I had been a skinny invalid child pushed around in a wheelchair. They hadn't kept pace with events it seemed.

When I stepped off the train at Euston, the whole family, comprising sundry aunts, uncles and cousins, converged on me in a protective mass, bustling me into a waiting taxi. I could see poor Brian bobbing and waving to me in the distance; he had come down to meet me. But the fates and my relatives were too strong for us, and I quickly found myself rattling off down the Balls Pond Road to the East End. The family were such a wonderful, loving and kind-hearted crowd, that I found it next to impossible to hurt their feelings. It took me several days to get over to them the idea that I was now an adult, no longer an invalid ... and especially wanted to meet my pal Brian, and go out to enjoy myself. Eventually the penny dropped. Brian and I were allowed to meet up as planned.

It was a great holiday. We went to the exhibition, the first of the great modern trade fairs. It was presided over by the silver cigar-shaped 'Skylon' which floated, without apparent means of support, over the hugely imaginative pavilions and the dome of discovery.

It was here, incidentally, that Brian and I saw our first 3-D film. It was a horror film called the 'House of Wax.' The audience was issued with red and green stereo spectacles, and some of the gruesome scenes became rather too close for comfort!

We spent time at the newly-opened Battersea fun fair. We saw St. Pauls' and tower bridge, and at night we went 'up West' to see a couple of shows. It was all quite an improvement on my last years' holiday, sitting disconsolately by the railway bridge near old Mr. Featherstoneghough's cottage in Wales (bless his heart). I have to say, the 1951 festival was also far better planned and organised (even given the harsh post-war, austere climate) than the Millennium celebrations some forty-nine years later, when Britain was in far better shape to have organised something spectacular ... but didn't.

It must not be supposed that those of my home town, Wallasey, were at all behindhand in celebrating The Festival of Britain Year. The town hall was illuminated, and the corporation sewage works was thrown open to the public (it's true so help me!). The piece-de-resistance of Liverpool's programme of festivities, was to be an ambitious seven-mile-long cavalcade of shipping, tugs, ferry boats, tankers, cargo boats, ..., even ocean liners, which were to steam majestically down the river and out into the bay. Perhaps half a million people lined both banks of the Mersey on the evening of the event.

Mum and I each paid £1 for seats in somebody's front garden, overlooking the river (a lot of money back then!). We sat down with folding chairs, a flask of tea and sandwiches (for £1 a head, you'd think they could've given us a cuppa and a butty!). It was not entirely successful. Put more bluntly, it was a bloomin' farce! Perhaps it had escaped the planners' attention, but the river estuary was over a mile wide at this point.

From where we sat, for all we could distinguish of the great armada, as they sailed out to sea in the evening mist, they might have been merely tiny black water beetles. Never mind, Mum's decanted tea and sandwiches were great!

About this time, Brian had his own little personal piece of history in the making; which he invited me to inspect one Sunday afternoon, in the front parlour where his frail and gentle old mum sat over her tea and scones.

The curtains were tightly shut, so once my eyes had became accustomed to the gloom, I saw a truly massive piece of apparatus. It was some four-foot-high at least, crammed full of valves, and a rats nest of multi-coloured bits of wire. Nestling at the heart of all this was a little cathode-ray tube, with a tiny screen maybe four-inches across. Brian flicked a switch, fiddled with half-a-dozen control knobs and a minute, pale-green image swam into view.

"Silvia Peters, the TV announcer!" announced Brian proudly.

It was the first television picture I had ever seen, and I was not altogether impressed. However, Brian had spent several months building the set from a design in 'Practical Wireless' and was, evidently, very proud of his achievement; probably the first owner of a TV set in his area. So, I acted suitably astounded. The idea that such a clumsy, expensive device with it's tiny flickering image could ever pose a threat to the mighty cinema industry would have appeared utter fantasy at that time. Yet within fifteen years, Television avalanched in popularity until eighty-percent of cinemas were forced out of business; and with them, the jobs of tens of thousands of workers like myself.

Having watched this new toy for a while, we switched off, got our coats and caps from the hall, and took the ferry across to Liverpool. The Marx Brothers were appearing in person at the Empire theatre! In those days, the live theatre was still very popular. The Empire, and similarly large-city-centre venues, often had first-class programmes. Major stars of the stage and screen would appear on stage to packed-houses. 'Television? Phooey!' we said ... give us the movies or real live entertainment every time!

Reel Sixteen

This Sunday only:

"The Reformer and the Redhead"

also

"The Skipper Surprises his Wife"

Next door to the Embassy cinema stood a small, dusty shop-front advertising 'Durex' and 'Brylcreem'. Surmounted by a Barbers' pole, swathed in red and white bandage, it proclaimed the presence of "Danny's Hairdressing Salon."

Mr. Danny Cohen, the proprietor, was a genial, bustling little man. He sported a ginger moustache and a gleaming bald pate, which positively twinkled as he darted about among clippers and combs. His wife, Golda, shared most of his characteristics, apart from the moustache and bald pate. She did Ladies' perms by appointment, in a mysterious little room behind the barber shop. Danny's salon was no hygiene-obsessed, chrome-plated, tonsorial clinic, as one might find today. Frankly, it was a little on the dingy side. The equipment was old and the paintwork hovered undecidedly between dirty green and an even dirtier grey. However, no-one seemed to mind.

Danny and Golda were a friendly, kind-hearted couple. Their patrons came from miles around for the customary shave, short-back-and-sides, a dab of Brylcreem and the latest local gossip. Most of the Embassy staff patronised Danny's place, in one way or another. Terrence and I quite got into the habit of popping in to see Danny, almost every day on our way to work; we came to know the family quite well.

A large and rapidly-growing family, all of which they provided for and sent off to University (they all did their old

Dad proud - doctors, lawyers, accountants ... all the usual). Naturally, Danny was always keen to find ways to supplement his income. He tinkered around in the second-hand trade, using his salon and its clientele as a base for his operations.

Many an unsuspecting patron of Danny's would emerge from his shop clean-shaven, well-trimmed and clutching an old bicycle tyre or sewing machine (which he'd had no thought of purchasing until Danny's persuasive manner got to work on him in the barber's chair). One day in particular, I found Danny happily snipping away to the strains of Billy Cotton's band - relayed on an imposing but very ancient 'wireless' set.

"Got it given to me by a customer, Phil." said Danny proudly. "Gave it a good blow out with me hairdryer, pushed all the valves in tight and now it's as good as new! Worth a couple of quid easy!"

Patting it proudly, two of the knobs fell clean off. Nevertheless, he sold the set; and, on the strength of this, decided to set himself up as a dealer of second-hand wireless sets. However, he soon found he had bitten off more than he could chew. Within a few weeks, the little salon was littered with stacks of aging Murphies, Philcos, Marconis, ... and so on; even some wartime austerity sets, no less.

"How's the business going Danny?" I asked, squeezing myself between the piles of old radio sets and into the chair for a quick trim.

"Well, not so good Phil." he admitted, scratching his pate. "Most of these sets have got something serious the matter with them. It would cost me a fortune to put them right. I don't suppose a proper repair man would even look at them ..."

Pondering for a moment, I hatched a cunning plan ... I had always wanted to do something in the electrical line, until the fates stepped in and thwarted my ambitions in that direction.

Now, was this my big chance? A friend of mine, Brian Coulter, had built a whole TV set from scratch. So I certainly ought to be able to do some simple radio repairs.

"Let me have a go at fixing one or two of them for you." I suggested.

Danny sent me staggering home with a couple of choice (but dumb) pre-war specimens to mend. The faults were not too difficult to fix, and I soon returned them to working order. Danny, delighted, gave me a few shillings for my trouble. With great gusto, we promptly set up a spare-time business together. Without sufficient spare time at home, I commandeered a corner of the operators' staff room at the Embassy as workshop space.

I set-to repairing Danny's varied flock of old radios, between spells manning the projector. Our chief, Stanley Briggs, was remarkably tolerant in some respects, provided we neglected no part of our proper duties. Our off-duty spells were no concern of his. I could, I suppose, have run a tripe dressing business from the staff room if so-minded, with as little opposition!

While I can't say I made much money out of my extra work repairing wireless sets, the experience I gained was wholly invaluable. I learned to read circuit diagrams and to diagnose more difficult faults. After a few months at it, I could claim to be a reasonably-competent radio repair man. So, I had Danny's pressing need for more cash, and Stan Briggs' tolerant attitude, to thank for starting me off on the road to my latter career as an electronics engineer.

Now and again, Stanley would recollect his tutorial duties as a chief, when he would say:

"Now Phil, it's time you stopped farting about with them old refugees from '2LO' and learned some projection theory."

Opening an old dog-eared textbook, referred to with some reverence as the 'operators bible', he would patiently go over basic formulae:

'Image size(w) is given by object size(p), times length to screen, and divided by focal length(f). The focal length of a compound lens is given by ... blah, blah, blah, ...'

He would go over the rules for calculating light intensity, or the curvature of a lens, minimising picture distortion (due to the the projector being high up and the screen low down), ..., and so on. Poor Stan might just as well have been talking to the old HMV radio, which stood mutely on the table between us. I could add and subtract, do a little simple multiplication and such; but that was about it! I knew nothing of sines, cosines and the simplest algebraic formulae, which might have been written in Sanscrit for all the meaning it had for me. All quite frustrating!

He would naturally come to the conclusion that I was as thick as two short planks; storming off to the 'Stanley Arms' to sooth his ruffled nerves, with a couple of pints of best bitter. Had Stan been a boastful man, he might well have bragged a bit about his almost unique possession: a twenty-year-old second operator, whose mathematical ability was limited to counting the change for the chips and cream soda. But Stan was a modest man, and he kept quiet about it, saving me much embarrassment.

In hindsight, I don't think I really was all that dim-witted. It was just that I was ... slightly unfortunate to have had a fragmented scholastic career. When I was just thirteen, and still living in the Welsh village with my parents, I had some qualms about the adequacy of my education (since I had not yet set foot inside a classroom). Mum hired Miss Madoc, one of the two local schoolteachers. She came along twice a week, after school, to teach me the rudiments of English grammar and arithmetic. She quickly learned, to her dismay, the sheer extent of my ignorance. I literally could not add together any numbers which came to a total of more than ten!

When she spoke of fractions, decimals, verbs and punctuation, I truthfully told her I had not the faintest idea about what she was saying.

Giving up, Miss Madoc enlisted the help of Mr. Thomas the headmaster. He persuaded my parents to let me attend the village school; at least on those days when I was well enough.

At last, I began to attend school for a few remaining months; before the official school leaving age of fourteen. I learned to sing Cym Rhondda and Sospan Bach in Welsh, to paint florid Welsh dragons for school posters, and to detest 'Oliver Twist' (as read in stretches of an hour at a time with dramatic emphasis by Mr. Thomas).

But I cannot say I made any real academic progress.

Even the little eight-year-olds were far more advanced than I in most subjects. Perhaps I should really have been in a lower class, but the desks were too small for me to fit my gangly legs behind.

This dilemma was resolved by the advent of VE day - the end of the war and a return to our old house back in Wallasey. Some intensive private tuition, backed up by a year or so at one of the new secondary modern schools, might have helped me catch up. Unfortunately, it was wrong decision time again! After some intensive lobbying of local council officials by my mother, I was admitted to the local school for handicapped children. Bollocks! This to ensure against my becoming overtired, catching a chill, having to eat bangers and mash or some other unjustified hardships.

Elleray Park school accommodated children with every type and degree of physical disability, from the age of six to fifteen. It did so in just three classrooms, and was run by a gaggle of middle-aged ladies, full of care and kindness towards their deprived pupils. They were determined (much as some teachers still are today) to not overtax our simple brains with academic learning. Instead we learned flower pressing, basket weaving, simple cookery and four-part versions of "Sweet Lass of Richmond Hill." There were no formal lessons in maths, science, foreign languages or indeed anything that could conceivably have been of use to us in the great big world outside.

Even though to me the school was clearly a well-intentioned flop, it did teach me a few useful lessons about life in general.

In particular, it brought home to me that, if my own childhood had been nothing to write home about, there were plenty of kids around a hell of a sight worse off. Two of my classmates died while still in their teens.

One ebullient, likable lad keeled over suddenly one day and died, as a result of a heart condition. The other, my closest friend at the school, was a chronic asthmatic. He died shortly after leaving school, with his dearest wish (confided to me in a whisper) unfulfilled; to kiss a pretty girl just once! The majority of the kids of course did get better as they grew older, and did very well in later life; in-spite the school's crazy curriculum.

Once I started work as a projectionist, and I began to realise just how academically dim I was, I tried in a half-hearted way to improve myself. I tried my hand at a correspondence course in basic maths and physics, only to chuck my hand in after a couple of months. "They may be called simple equations," I stormed at the Correspondence School's agent "but I'm buggered if I can understand them!"

However, later on at the Embassy cinema, with it's extra time-off, night school was a possibility. I signed on and stuck it out for a couple of terms. However, by then I was involved in pamphleteering for the Young Conservatives and holding hands with my first girl friends. Night school came a poor third, so I gave it up. Lack of purpose, that was my trouble. I could have done worse than follow the example of Micky Flack, who, for sheer persistence and single-mindedness, should have been my ideal role-model.

Micky was a corporation bus driver and a rabid ornithologist. He came up to the operating box one evening, asking if he might make some sketches of the arc lamps on our projectors. He came back a few days later asking for the loan of some partly-used carbon rods from the lamps.

Before he left, Micky asked, with some little diffidence, if I would like to go along to his house when next I had time off to see something he had built. I was very curious and agreed at once to pop round. He lived in a small council house down by the docks along with his long-suffering wife and several kids.

On Sunday morning was my visit, and I found Micky busily engaged in some experiment in their tiny front room. A home-made arc lamp hissed and spluttered on the dining table, giving out a blinding white glare. Micky twiddled with a Heath-Robinson-like array of knobs and levers to adjust it. The room was insufferably hot due to the row of electric fires wired in series with the arc lamp to absorb the surplus voltage from the mains. The arc lamp required about 30-volts, while the mains was the usual 240-volt supply. So, the difference had to be dissipated by the electric heaters, each making the whole room quite like the inside of a sauna bath.

Micky explained his project, while perspiration ran down our faces. As a keen bird fancier, he had collected a huge number of photos and drawings of exotic birds. His ambition was to build an epidiascope - that is a projector which will throw an enlarged image onto a screen of any photo, or whatever is popped into it. His idea was to give illustrated talks on his pet subject to like-minded enthusiasts.

The problem was how to get a sufficiently intense white light to bounce off even the dullest old print. An arc lamp, such as that used at the Embassy cinema, seemed the obvious answer.

Micky smiled at my congratulations on his ingenuity, but then self-doubt assailed him ...

"What can I do about the ruddy heat from these bloody electric fires? It's driven the wife and kids into the back yard, and she's complaining about not being able to do her ironing out there."

I had an idea. Explaining to Micky that we used salt-water dash pots at the Embassy to absorb surplus voltage, when the house lights were being dimmed, he immediately seized on the idea gratefully. Micky and I hurried out into the cool fresh air.

When I stopped by a few days later, to see how he was progressing, it was definitely cooler in the front room, but more than a little foggy (in fact the entire front room, hallway and stairs was a wash with steamy vapour).

Moisture trickled down the wallpaper and plopped onto the Lino floor. The wife and kids could just be made out as ghostly outlines, through the open kitchen door. The cause of all this murkiness was a large earthenware sink, sat on the floor and filled with salt water; it was absorbing the surplus voltage for the arc lamp in place of the old electric fires. The water hissed and bubbled most violently, like a miniature witches cauldron.

I looked on in dismay, as the danger of instant electrocution, from any sudden careless movement, was such that I shudder even now to remember it.

"I'm afraid we still haven't got it right Phil." said Micky gloomily. "The missus is getting quite narky about all this steam. Says it's making her curls come out."

Micky adjusted the arc lamp, and we peered through the mist at some prized pictures of (I believe) the lesser spotted slopgorbler, or something. The salt water hissed and gurgled behind us. Mrs. Flack yelled at us from the kitchen and a neighbour banged on the party wall.

"'Er lights go out next door when I switch this thing on ..." explained Micky.

"It's no bloody good. I give up!" said Micky at last in disgust, as he switched off the arc lamp and put his photos away.

Thinking hard ... I suggested:

"What about a transformer? Like we use in the cinema! That should solve all your problems. Shop around at the war surplus stores and you should be able to pick one up for just a few bob. You may have to rewind it with some thicker wire to take the heavy arc lamp current, but that's not too difficult. You can throw away the electric fires and the salt water bath. The transformer will change the 240 volts down to 30 volts for your arc lamp without any bother, and bob will most definitely be your uncle!"

On my next visit, I found that Micky had bought his transformer. It lay in a great heap of rusty iron plates and coils of greasy wire all over the living room floor. The rest of the family were, as usual, exiled to the back kitchen.

"What about the thick wire for the thirty-volt arc lamp winding?" I asked.

"Come on!" Micky said enthusiastically, dragging me into the tiny back yard. "Just look at this!"

Festoons of thick copper wire were clothes-pegged to the washing line, draped over the dustbin, the coal shed and everything in sight. A large pot of black varnish and a paint brush rested on the seat of the outside loo while thick, treacly varnish dripped from the suspended wires with a soft pattering sound like sooty April showers.

"I could only get bare copper wire," explained Micky, "so I'm having to insulate it with varnish myself. Three or four coats should do it!"

Back in the house, I smiled at Mrs. Micky (I never learned of her real name), but I sensed her fist clenching and managed to beat a hasty retreat. She had obviously begun to associate my visits with each fresh domestic disaster; like a sort of wicked fairy in cloth cap and sports jacket.

"She's having to use the clothes line next door for her washing." whispered Micky as we parted.

In the end, Micky got his transformer working, finished his epidiascope, cleaned up all the mess and got the family back into the front room again. He became well-known in the locality for his illustrated talks on birds. I am not a bird fancier myself but I believe he was particularly celebrated for his projected images of the mating dance of the shorter-legged oomagoolie bird, or some such ornithological disparity.

I only wish I'd had just one-quarter of Micky's dogged persistence in those days. Had I carried on with my studies like a sensible lad, who knows what heights I might have scaled by now ... architect, a High Court Judge, perhaps even a bank manager? But alas, it was pig-ignorance and projectors for me for some years to come ... and that did serve me right too!

Reel Seventeen

All this week:

"Annie Get Your Gun"

Plus

"Popeye" the cartoon.

"And a-one-two-three, one-two-three ... keep it up lads, keep it up!"

On one side of the parquet dance floor, a couple of dozen shambling, clumsy, perspiring gentlemen; elegantly led by Mr. Albert Jackson, in the basic steps of the waltz. On the far side of the room Mrs. Jackson, elaborately coiffured and ablaze with sequins, twirled the ladies through the corresponding steps.

"Right lads. That will do. I think most of you have got the hang of that chassis movement now."

Albert, delicately mopping his brow with a small silk handkerchief, stalked gravely over to join Mrs. Jackson in the centre of the floor.

Her sister Bettina, seated stiff and prim at the upright rosewood in the corner, launched into a hammer-clavier version of 'When you are in love (two, three) it's the loveliest night of the year.' Taking our partners, we stumbled into a parody of a slow waltz across the dance floor.

"Mr. Rosen, I'm afraid you're treading on my feet again. I've already got a plaster on my toe from the last time!"

"Dreadfully sorry Miss P'P'Pringleton." I stammered, managing to thwack a perfectly innocent old gentleman on the ear with my elbow.

Miss Pringleton had iron-grey hair, done up into a tight bun, and wore a trailing long dress. She also smelled of lavender and mothballs. I should like to bequeath her to the nice old gentleman ... he who is being hurled around the floor, by the energetic young lady with the big bust (no coarse language here you will note). But, of course, I would not dream of hurting Miss Pringleton's feelings.

My chance came some weeks later when 'Miss P' was absent with a dose of Flu; and Bernice joined the class, initially partnerless. I almost fell-over myself to volunteer my services. Bernice was about my age with a jolly personality. She was pretty, with a figure that hovered between 'voluptuous' and 'slightly podgy.' We got on very well together, and I tried my hardest to not damage her or anyone else during our dance-like gyrations.

Three weeks later 'Miss P' returned. She had a right ding-dong with my new partner, since she felt that Bernice had stolen her property! It was wholly embarrassing, although not entirely unflattering. Having rushed off to the bog to leave them all to it, I returned to find, thankfully, that the Jacksons had smoothed things over and found a middle-aged gentleman for Miss P (whose previous partner had gone off with Sciatica). Bernice sat quietly victorious, powdering her nose and it was all rather baffling; especially since Miss P always kept banging on about how I had trodden on her toes. You might have thought she'd be glad to be rid of me ... surely?

I had joined the Greenbank Dancing Academy, New Brighton, about the middle of my second year at the Embassy Cinema. This, in the vain hope that I might improve my social standing with the local birds. At twenty years-of-age, I was still ornithologically bereft. Apart from everything else, to be Judy-less was hurtful to one's ego (a bit like not owning a motor bike or a decent set of golf clubs).

The trouble was, as many of my professional colleagues found, you couldn't do much in the way of chatting up a nice bit of stuff ... when one had only five or six free nights a month in which to do so. How any of the older projectionists managed to find the right girl, court her and get to march her up the aisle, was a profound mystery to me. It must have required a special kind of high-speed technique which ... I apparently didn't possess.

I tried of course. There was Mary Donaghue: gentle and attractive, whose twin passions were classical music and making splints for injured birds. We met at the Young Conservatives Club and, since I fully shared her first interest, we got on very well together (my long hours spent peering at Scoop-warblers in Micky's epidiascope taught me to tolerate the second).

We went to concerts together at the Liverpool Philharmonic and, as I mended her old bird cages, we were good company for each-other; albeit in a platonic way. It was the parrot that was responsible for ending our innocent friendship ... that and Mary's father so it happened ...

Old Captain Donaghue was a retired sea dog, a martinet where household discipline was concerned and, somehow, suspected the trustworthiness of all foreigners such as Jews, coloured folk and Scotsmen. Coming as I did, rather unmistakably, from the first category, it was judged wisest for us to no longer meet. So, Mary waited until one afternoon, when the captain was supposed to be out somewhere, before asking me round for afternoon tea ... lovely!

Well, there I sat contentedly listening to Brahms on Mary's record player. With my mouth full of omelette and brown buttered bread, I was sandwiched between a baleful-eyed parrot and a rather restless budgie. Suddenly, the front door opened and slammed-to with a crash that sent Mary starting to her feet in consternation.

"It's Daddy!" she cried. "Quick, into the garden. Take your omelette with you, eat it behind the potting shed. I'll whistle like this 'phwee, phwee' when he goes up to his study. Then you'll be safe to come back in."

The parrot looked on, in grim satisfaction, as I shot out into the garden with my omelette, bread and butter and now a fairy cake also balanced on the plate. After a few minutes, I heard the pre-arranged whistle 'Phwee Phwee' and walked back confidently into the kitchen ...

... slap-bang into the bushy eyebrows and foul-tempered countenance of the Captain.

Mary was nowhere to be seen when "Phwee Phwee" went the parrot, with a seemingly self-satisfied smirk!

"Just called to fix the sparrow's crutches ..." I mumbled and hurried out, fast!

After our initial setback, Mary and I tended to restrict our friendship to companionable chats about Brahms and Budgies, while folding election leaflets for the Y.Cs.

Yes, girl friends, steady or unsteady, were by no means easy to acquire as far as I was concerned. The dancing school didn't help all that much either. I continued to patronise Mr. Jackson's class for a few months, but never managed to progress beyond the first few steps of the waltz and quickstep. Later, when the class settled down to serious work for bronze and silver medals, Mr. Jackson tactfully suggested that perhaps I was "being taken beyond my capabilities." I took the hint and left.

I took Bernice to the odd Saturday night hop, at the Tower Ballroom, and even went so far, on one occasion, as to peck her on the cheek in an especially passionate moment. The feeble affair finally fizzled-out when Bernice found a handsome Merchant Navy Officer as her new dancing partner.

He was a keen enthusiast and, together, they went on from strength-to-strength, winning medals galore for the daring and versatility of their movements. Of course, they probably did quite a bit of dancing as well!

Our Second Op. Terrence, was quite a keen dancer himself. He was particularly good at the Samba, which I should have liked to learn. The Jackson's had put the blockers on this for me, after I had managed to bring down no less than three other couples with one ill-advised twirl. Good-hearted Terrence offered to teach me the Samba. For several nights, the Embassy patrons endured an exclusively South American programme, blared out during the intervals on the non-sync, while Terrence gravely took me through the basic steps - around Number One projector, a quick twirl round the rectifier cubicle, a snappy glide past the fire extinguisher, past Number Two projector, then off we go again ...

The lessons were brought to an abrupt end when Stan Briggs, the chief, arrived in the box unexpectedly. We were prancing up and down (Terrence leading), when his jaw dropped in ludicrous dismay ...

"Jesus! I haven't got a pair of bleedin' Jessies have I? Don't tell me that. I couldn't stand it!"

Once we had explained ...

"A couple of great soft kids, that's what you are. Don't let me catch you capering around again ... you could 'ave easily damaged yourselves or the equipment ..."

Stan's mutterings died away as he tottered-off downstairs, to soothe his ruffled nerves once again at the Stanley Arms a few doors up the road.

Terrence was staring dreamily into space. I knew that look - some new enthusiasm was about to erupt at any moment.

"Kids - dancing! I've got it! Alright the sweet shop idea didn't work but how's about this for a great idea Phil? You know all those teenage kids that hang about the street at weekends with nothing to do except get into trouble?

Well, we'll run Sunday afternoon hops for them (the term 'disco' had yet to be born). "We'll put up some decorations, bring in a record player, I'll bring in the records, you can play them for me ... my sister Betty will sell them crisps and bottles of pop. We'll print proper tickets, charge, say, a shilling entrance ... spot prizes, a talent contest ..." Terrence almost foamed at the mouth in his excitement.

"Calm down Terrence, there's a good lad." I said. "Just where are you planning to hold these ballroom extravaganzas?"

Terrence grinned sheepishly, walking over to lace up his machine, while I put the Samba records away loading the non-sync with the more customary sedate piano medleys.

Behind the Embassy, across a sort of mildewy, weed-infested courtyard, stood a small building not unlike a long-neglected scout hut in appearance. It was owned by the cinema but it was never used, no-one had been near it for years. Terrence's idea in brief was to get Mr. O'Brian's permission to do the place up, and run his dances on Sunday afternoons before first-house claimed our attention. I say 'our attention' because Terrence, as always, took it absolutely for granted that Bill Swift and I would help him with all of his daft schemes.

I wasn't at all happy at the thought of being stuck with a mass of screaming jostling teenagers, least of all in that tiny hut. Not when I should have been relaxing after my Sunday lunch. The trouble was that giving the cold shoulder to Terrence, during one of his fits of enthusiasm, was pretty much-impossible.

So, it was easier to muck-in and lend a hand; even though one knew instinctively that catastrophe in some form or other lay just around the corner. So, in our off-duty hours we set to ...

We cleaned the place up and put up some paper decorations, left over from a past Christmas party. I rigged up a home-made amplifier, and record player, and made some nice advertising posters to stick in Danny's barber shop window.

The grand opening passed off surprisingly well. Three or four dozen assorted kids turned up, all in a clean and well-behaved condition. They jigged around to Terrence's brand new jive, and rock and roll records, and scoffed a prodigious amount of crisps and cream soda. By five O'Clock in the afternoon we played 'God save the King' and shoved the kids out; cleaned up all the litter and crossed the courtyard to start our normal evening's work.

Terrence ran several of these primordial Discos, and even managed to show a small profit. The youngsters were now showing up on a regular basis. For once, all was going well. Then Terrence, as usual, overreached himself.

"I hope you won't feel offended Phil," he said, as we were mucking out the arc lamps one morning, "but I don't think that amplifier thing of yours is really loud enough. Some of the kids complain that when they're yelling really loud, they can't hear the music at the same time."

"Isn't that their fault?" I suggested mildly.

"Well perhaps it is, but I think I've got the answer!" exclaimed Terrence. "We'll have a real band instead of the canned music. Just a small band of course, and I know just the lads for the job. They're very cheap and it'll be a great new attraction for the kids."

I thought the idea to be plain balmy. By the time one fitted-in even just a four-piece band, with all their instruments, a lemonade and crisps stall and someone at the door to take the money, the kids would be forced to dance outside. Terrence was, of course, deaf to all carping criticisms of this kind. He went ahead with his plans and even went so far as to invite Stan Briggs, our chief, to bring his old Banjo along to augment the group (a suggestion which that worthy declined with some quite unnecessarily coarse language). However, as the first 'live music' Sunday approached I was sure I could detect signs of unease on Terrence's part; although he strenuously denied there was anything wrong.

As it happened, the films were late arriving that Sunday. So, I spent part of the afternoon in the re-wind room making up that evening's programme. When finished, I hurried over to the 'Palais' to hear what the band sounded like. Gingerly opening the door to the little hut, I was half-expecting to be blown off my feet by the blare of drums and saxophone ... it was ominously quiet.

I entered, and there in a corner, quite alone, sat a dear old lady in a long, faded evening gown and grey woolly cardigan (thrown over to keep out the evening chill). She was gently tinkling away at a battered upright piano. The melodies she played reminded me at once of the songs my Mum used to sing when I was a kid (long forgotten tunes from romantic old pre-war musicals). On the other-side of the room, the natives were getting decidedly restless.

"What happened to the band?" I whispered to a worried and fidgety Terrence. "They let me down. Went off to another engagement. Higher fee I suppose. I got Miss Heathersage here to come along at the last minute. She's a friend of my Mum you know. Mum said Miss Heathersage used to go down a treat at the dances they had at her old folks' club. Only trouble is she doesn't know any modern pop music at all!"

As the restlessness of the natives increased ...

"Can't you play nothin' more groovy than that missus?" demanded a truculent, trainee teddy boy. His enquiry met with a chorus of marked approval from those around him.

"I'm afraid not young man," said Miss Heathersage mildly, "I'm not even sure if I know what 'groovy' means."

At this, things began to get nasty. Crisp bags and lemonade cups were hurled around, mostly in Terrence's direction. A chair or two was overturned, the decorations were torn down and then, mercifully, the the kids began to leave; at first in ones and twos, and then in a wild jostling melee that threatened to tear the rusty old door off it's hinges.

One of the last out was a young lady of perhaps fourteen- or fifteen-years-old, wearing a demure party dress and pink ribbons in her hair. As she trotted past us on her way out, she turned to Terrence and said:

"That was a soddin' awful dance that was, and I'm never going to come to another bleedin' one of 'em again, so there!" She blew a piercing raspberry, slammed the door and disappeared with her friends; leaving Terrence, Miss Heathersage and I alone with our thoughts.

I helped Terrence clean up the debris, then left him to escort dear old Miss Heathersage back to her top-floor flat, in nearby Egremont. I then hurried back to the Embassy to start the evening show.

The dances were finished, that was for sure, and for some days Terrence seemed quite cast down and far from his usual cheery self.

"I need a change, that's what!" exclaimed Terrence, as he gloomily patched together the mangled remains of a much-worn Three Stooges comedy film. "I need some excitement, pastures-new and all that sort of thing."

The following day Terrence announced, with some excitement, to Stan Briggs and I, that the pastures new had been established. "I'm leaving for a new job." Said Terrence.

"I'm sorry to hear that." said Stanley. "Where are you buggering off to then?"

"I'm starting next week at Young's sausage factory, as a trainee sausage stuffer."

"And good luck to you." said Stan with a straight face, offering a warm handshake.

We didn't bother with the customary farewell party - the cream buns, cream soda and all that lot. Somehow we were all of us sure, that before too long, Terrence would be back among us again.

Reel Eighteen

All this week:

"Arsenic and Old Lace"

Plus

"Tomahawk"

When Terrence left the glamorous world of show business, to take up the gentle art of sausage stuffing, it left a gap in our ranks which Stanley Briggs had some difficulty filling. Bill Swift was considered too young to be promoted to full second Op, so he was just given a small rise in salary, to compensate for the extra responsibility he would incur on my days off. We advertised for a new third operator, which revealed a most interesting insight into a section of humanity (which social workers sometimes referred to as having 'personality problems').

Jim Worral, who joined us after answering our first advert, was something of an enigma. He somehow just didn't fit in. He was a tall, good-looking bloke in his late twenties. He wore a yachting blazer and grey sports flannels, sporting an expensive tie with an old-school crest emblazoned on it.

He puffed away at a massive briar pipe in the contemplative manner of an Oxford don. He might have been the sports master at some expensive private school, or at least something in the banking or insurance line. But, a third projectionist at £3 per week? There was something wrong somewhere.

Still, Jim was quiet, friendly and nicely spoken. He carried out the simple tasks of a junior Op. without complaint. After the first few days our reserve melted away and we accepted him; posh accent, briar pipe an' all.

But, after a week or two, we came to realise what was the matter with him ... why he had dropped Icarus-like into our lowly-paid midst, from whatever middle-class professional circles he had once ornamented. He was a hopeless alcoholic. He never became rude or boisterous; but he would appear in the box in the evening glassy eyed, slurring his speech and reeking of whiskey. Stan felt sorry for him, trying to persuade him to keep tolerably sober during working hours at least. It was no use. Jim got steadily worse until it became difficult to trust him with any sort of responsible task.

The crunch came one night when, as ill-luck would have it, Stan was off duty and I was in charge. We were showing one of those awful Hollywood gangster films as the 'A' feature: one of those films where all the male characters wear trilby hats, speak out the corner of their mouths and produce revolvers from their pockets as nonchalantly as an Englishman would his pipe. The 'B' film was a pop musical full of college teenagers, crooners, jitterbugging and ... similar horrors. The programme totaled fourteen reels of film and Jim had made up the programme that afternoon when it was piously hoped he would be in a reasonably sober state.

Talk about a night to remember! It was a most unforgettable experience, both for the audience and for us in the box that night. There was scarcely one reel in it's right place in the programme. The two main feature films were inextricably mixed up with each other, and out of sequence. Bill and I tried frantically to get the reels into the right order ... while the alarm buzzer, operated from the back stalls by mystified usherettes, almost flew off the wall in noisy protest. After some three-quarters-of-an-hour of this bedlam, Mr. O'Brian (until then blissfully unaware while counting up the takings in his secluded office) was informed that all was not well and came storming up to the box in a fury.

He took in the scene at a glance - Bill and I working like Trojans, red-faced, perspiring and knee-deep in film, while poor Jim lay draped over one of the projectors snoring peacefully in a drunken stupor.

Mr. O'Brian stalked over to Jim, picked him up off the machine and, with deep disdain, shook him awake; telling him he was to consider himself instantly dismissed. Jim looked confusedly around him, found his coat and stumbled downstairs. We never saw him again.

A few days later, I went round to Jim's lodgings with his last week's pay packet, his insurance cards and his old briar pipe. He wasn't in; but his sister, a pale, sickly-looking girl, thanked me for my trouble and invited me into the bottle-strewn front room. She gave me a potted history of her brother's troubles. It seemed he had been a radio officer in the navy, and doing well career-wise until the 'demon drink' got it's claws into him. Jim had been on the dole (unemployment benefit) for some time, before seeing Mr. O'Brian's advert. He remembered the shipboard film shows he used to run and so applied for the job at the Embassy.

"God only knows what will happen to him now." She said sadly. I left, hoping that somehow or other Jim would pull through. He was too nice a chap to finish up with the D.Ts in some ghastly asylum.

We advertised again. Mr. Leonard Stonebridge turned up, and was accepted as our next junior operator. He also had a problem and one didn't need to be a trained psychologist to diagnose what it was. The man was suffering from an acute attack of sheer grinding poverty. I had never seen anyone, outside a Dickensian novel, who so exuded the very essence and flavour of poverty to the extent that Lennie did. He was in his mid-thirties, painfully thin with uncombed hair and a dirty stubble on his chin. His clothes, patched and patched again, had the look of coming straight off the Corporation rubbish tip.

Bill and I felt dreadfully sorry for him, doing what we could to help. We shared our sandwiches with him, gave him unwanted ties, shirts and shoes, and generally tried to cheer him up a bit.

He told us he lived in a two-roomed flat with his invalid father, and was finding it a dreadful struggle to make ends meet. He could, he said bitterly, have got more on the dole than as a junior projectionist; but it was the only work he could do and he didn't believe in accepting charity, even of the state variety. As the weeks went by, we could see that things were getting ever more difficult for Lennie. I guessed that what little food he could afford, went to keep his sick father going.

At last he plucked up the courage to ask Mr. O'Brian for a rise. Our manager was sympathetic, but explained gently that there was a certain going rate for the job, that at present there was no vacancy at a more senior post in the company, and so at £3 per week his salary would have to stay.

Lennie thanked Mr. O'Brian politely and said he quite understood. He went home to his two-bedroomed flat, gave his father his tea and made him comfortable. Then he took some cord, tied it to a hook in the ceiling and hanged himself.

Quite naturally, we were shattered by this tragedy. When Mr. O'Brian could bring himself to advertise yet again, we landed Ted Grafter (as it turned out a most appropriate name). He was what we used to call a 'wide boy' - up to every dodge for coining a few quid, by any means short of downright crime. Things fell off the back of a lorry into his outstretched hands with astonishing regularity. Whatever you wanted; cheap fags, pens, watches, dirty photos, ..., you name it, Ted Grafter had it, or could get it. He could well have been the prototype for Private Walker in 'Dad's Army'. Ted was a sallow-faced lad in his late twenties, sporting a fashionable Teddy-boy moustache and sideboards. He affected an air of swaggering self-confidence, which could become very irritating in the close confines of the operating box. What he was doing as a junior projectionist, was a mystery; unless, as we surmised, it was a useful cover for his questionable activities.

He had no respect whatever for our Chief Stanley Briggs. Many a stand-up row erupted between them over Stan's little rule book, and Ted's determination to totally ignore it ...

Stanley: "'Ere! That's no way to clean the viewing ports. First you wipe the dust off, then you smear on the Windolene, then you ..."

Ted, interrupting rudely: "Sod off! I'm doing it my way and that's good enough for me!"

Stan: "You impudent bugger, I'm the boss here and if I tell you to do a thing my way, that's how you do it, see?"

Ted would walk slowly up to purple-faced Stan, pat him gently and say "There, there Stanley. Remember your ulcers. You get off your bike too often, that's your trouble. Just calm down or you'll do yourself a mischief."

"'oo gets off his bike?" Stan would splutter furiously.

"You do, you silly old bugger!" Ted would retort calmly, and turn away to cary on with his work, whistling cheerfully all the while.

Such scenes as this became regular features of life in the box while Ted was with us. Stan might pop his ulcers or become apoplectic, but fire him he couldn't. We had already two major problem cases in the box. Who knew what kind of weirdo might turn up next if Ted were given the push? So there was nothing for it but for Stan to grit his teeth after such encounters, then rush off in defeat to the Stanley Arms to drown his sorrows.

While all this excitement was afoot, I stood quietly in the wings as one of life's little milestones passed me by: my 21st birthday. I had now been a projectionist for four-and-a-half years. I could now officially claim to have my own key to the door to let myself in. It was the age of majority. To mark the occasion, I gave a little tea party at my house. Guests included my old mates Wally Tate and Ronnie Summers from the Continental; Terrence and Bill from the Embassy; and, of course, my pal Brian Coulter.

I remember there were banana sandwiches, a big bowl of trifle, home-made fairy cakes and, of course, gallons of cream soda lemonade.

We played darts and pontoon, and I put on some Micky Katz jazz records (which, being in Yiddish, had only limited appeal). The night was still young so we decided to go out. It was unanimously agreed that there was only one possible way to commemorate such an important event as my 21st: second house at the palatial Odeon cinema in town to see 'Oklahoma'.

The complete absence of the fairer sex from my twenty-first birthday rave-up will not have gone unnoticed by the observant reader. It was not that we were misogynists, nor that the fairy cakes had gone to our heads. It was just that ... well I still hadn't got a girl friend, and probable that my guests thought it tactful to leave their own behind on that occasion. Although I kept on with my bird-catching activities, like Mozart's Papageno I ran into all sorts of unexpected difficulties.

I first met Rachel at a children's Purim party at our Synagogue. The children were traditionally rewarded by a film show and refreshments. I was roped into run the Popeye cartoons, while Rachel was handing out sticky buns. When we first met - she was only seventeen, and a keen amateur singer with a sweet voice. While the children were wolfing-down their goodies, she sang Cherubino's Aria to the admiring Mums and Dads. With her brown eyes and dimpled cheeks, I found her presence wholly distracting.

The film was old and brittle and, with my inattention, I had a couple of mishaps in quick succession. As the children

became increasingly fractious ... "Damn!" I said in exasperation.
The Mums tut-tutted their displeasure at my outburst. Rachel just refreshingly giggled.

The following Sunday afternoon, Brian Coulter and I were watching a cricket match in Central park ... not that I knew anything about the game. To me the match was about as incomprehensible as a Papuan tribal dance.

But it was sunny and peaceful, and it seemed as good a place as any to get some fresh air, before plunging into the operating box for six hours of smoky gloom (and those dreadful Sunday 'B' feature films). Then, I spotted Rachel sitting nearby. She was also watching the match when I strolled over quite nonchalantly to sit down beside her.

"H-h-how ..." I began, then quickly lapsed into total incoherence. Brian came to my rescue by discussing with Rachel some crisis in the game, which had to do with a googly ... which the silly mid-off had lobbed into the square leg or some such nonsense. I rallied and, plunging in at the deep end, asked her if she fancied coming out with me to a concert at the Philharmonic.

"They're playing Mossolov's night shift in a steel foundry." I explained eagerly. Rachel giggled and said "Fine."

I took Rachel out to several concerts, and was quite becoming infatuated with her. However, no surprise ... my nemesis was at hand ...

While outside the Embassy one day, teetering on top of a ladder fixing the foyer lights, I struggled to undo the screws of a bowl-shaped light fitting. Suddenly it came loose, drenching my upturned face with dirty brown rainwater and dead flies. I heard a well known giggle below and, wiping the water out of my eyes, saw Rachel walking by on the arm of her stout, prosperous and dignified dad.

"Hi Rachel. Hi Mr. Baron." I called, waving a muddy hand in greeting. Mr. Barron looked up, took in my ancient dungarees and patched old working jacket, sniffed audibly and, with Rachel's arm tucked firmly in his, proceeded majestically on his way.

"Sorry Phil," said Rachel on the phone next day, "but Daddy says I must concentrate on my studies and my singing lessons, so I won't be able to see you ..."

Come to think of it, Mr. Baron would have been very remiss in his parental duties if he hadn't come the heavy-handed father, in the way that he did. It was all very right and proper.

"And so much" I thought "for the nice Yiddish girl mum's always on about. I'm no blooming catch, that's for sure!"

Meanwhile back at the Embassy, Mabel Rudge had joined the staff as trainee usherette. I chummed-up with her after the Rachel affair out of pique; perhaps because she was about as big a contrast as possible. Mabel (well who can help their name, it's not their fault) was about twenty-five years old, a brassy blonde and unattached. She was fond of monkeys, so we would go off to surreptitiously feed butties to the chimps at the New Brighton Tower zoo. Then, one day, the truth came out. Mabel had a secret passion, and she wheeled her secret out for my inspection behind the Embassy one morning.

"I call it Cyril" she said, patting it proudly. 'Cyril' was a large, powerful motorbike of a size and ferocity that would have made a New York speed cop blanch. It certainly scared the daylights out of me!

"I do a fair bit of speedway racing in me spare time." said Mabel, as she donned her gauntlets, goggles and crash helmet. "Hop up behind Phil. We'll just have time for a quick flip up to New Brighton zoo and back before we're needed for the matinee."

I backed away in terror. "Not scared are you?" asked Mabel, eyeing my pale features with some surprise.

"Me? No! Whatever gave you that idea?" I climbed up behind Mabel, trying to recall the Hebrew prayer for deliverance from travel dangers, but couldn't remember anything about motorbikes in the liturgy.

"Here we go!" said Mabel. We roared off down the Seacombe shopping street, in a fog of dust and exhaust fumes; then across town at a sickening speed, swerving around careless pedestrians and screaming to a spine-jarring halt at traffic lights. Then away again, threading our way at a comfortable sixty MPH between opposing streams of traffic.

"Thanks for the ride Mabel," I croaked when we reached New Brighton, "but I think I'll take the number fourteen bus back home if you don't mind."

Next day Mrs. Rodgers, the senior usherette, took me aside in a mysterious manner.

"I think you ought to know that Mabel is, err ... not quite what she seems to be. I'm afraid she is rather a fast young lady."

"They don't come any faster," I agreed, "not without getting six months for speeding anyway."

"I do not refer to Mabel's motorbiking. What I think you ought to know is that she is engaged to a young man training to be a boiler maker in Newcastle. So it wouldn't be at all right for you to be associating with each other."

"I couldn't agree more Mrs. Rogers." I said cheerfully, seeing an easy way out of my dilemma. "We'll stop associating with each other right away!"

"Bloody old cow that Mrs. Rogers, ..." said Mabel angrily, waylaying me on my way to the box that night "... lecturing me as though I was a kid. I wasn't having any though. Told her to stick a sixpenny cornet up her fanny!"

Next day Mabel left by mutual agreement with the management, taking her motorbike with her. We later heard from a reliable source that Mabel had landed a spare time job as stand-in at the New Brighton fair wall of death! Come to think of it, many of my early girl friends were a bit weird in one way or another. I can remember that even my very first girl friend was weird. Her name as I recall was 'Babs'. We lay in adjoining beds in the children's ward of Wallasey Cottage Hospital. We were about seven years-old; she having her mastoids fixed, me having my asthma attended to.

"Thee thith toy alarm clock?" lisped Babs. "Well if I wee intho the littl' hole inthe top ..." (being remarkably dextrous, Babs was able to suit action to words), "yes, if I wee into the little hole I can make it go 'gurgle, gurgle' instead of 'bringg, bringg'."

And that, I think, as regards the early women in my life, was about par for the course ...

Ted Grafter left the Embassy much to the relief of Stan Briggs' ulcers. Ted left to become chief Op. at another local cinema and, on his last morning with us, made a valedictory speech to Stan which he had evidently stored up for some weeks. As I recall, he called Stan a lazy, petty-minded autocrat who should have been put out to grass years ago. However, it would be quite impossible to put Stan's spiteful response into cold print ...

When Ted left, Stan sat down heavily and mopped his brow. "Jesus!" he said brokenly, "This place is getting worse than a Sally Army hostel. What with drunks, nut cases and roughs like 'im that's just left, I really don't know what we're going to do."

Terrence popped his head in. "Morning all!" he said cheerfully.

Stan sprang to his feet, struggling to cajole his facial muscles into a smile of welcome.

"Come in Terrence lad. Good t'see you. Sit down and tell us how you're getting on. Not been made redundant by any chance?" he added hopefully.

"Well," admitted Terrence ruefully, "that's why I've come here. There's a temporary setback in the sausage stuffing line, and I'm not up to the black pudding packing jobs; too much skilled craftwork involved you see. So I was wondering ..."

"Say no more," said Stan shaking Terrence's hand and thumping his back in unfeigned delight at having him around again. "Welcome home Terrence lad. I can't tell you what a relief it is, after all we've been through since you left, to have a normal, sensible, well-balanced person like yourself to rely on in the box."

As Einstein once said:

"Philosophers play with the word, like a child with a doll ... It does not mean that everything in life is relative."

On this occasion, I would have to disagree ... relatively-speaking, Stan's assessment was quite right!

Reel Nineteen

All this week:

"Man in the White Suit"

also

A full supporting programme ...

"Brothers! Please give me your full, undivided attention, for what I have to say is of the utmost ..." to a roar of:

"Can't 'ear yer"
"What's 'ee say?"
"Speak up mate!"

"I SAID WHAT I HAVE TO SAY IS VERY IMPORTANT. SO PLEASE BROTHERS STOP TALKING AMONGST YOURSELVES AND LISTEN TO ME ... Thank you. That's, that's much better"

The crowd gradually desisted with "I can 'ear 'im now alright. It's just that I'm a bit mutt and Jeff from the projector noise see."

"Brothers, the Association of Cinema Proprietors has turned us down flat."

"Shame. Lousy rotten buggers!" exclaimed the crowd.

"Brothers please ... they say they can't afford any increase in basic rates of pay, or any reduction in working hours. Now they may not be millionaires, but they are a darned sight better off than we are!"

The crowd concurred in a uniform cheer ... "Aaaayyyyy!"

"Of course they can afford to pay us more, and it's up to all of us here to make damn sure they do!"

The crowd roared with enthusiastic applause.

With evident satisfaction, the dapper little NATKE district organiser surveyed the sea of enthusiastic faces before him. He was balanced precariously on a table, laid on an undergrowth of cruets and sauce bottles, in the restaurant of Liverpool's huge Odeon cinema. It was eleven O'Clock on a chilly winter's morning, and a time when the place would normally be empty and silent. Today the room was almost unbearably hot and stuffy, crammed to the doors with projectionists and doormen from just about every cinema on Merseyside. This was men's work! Usherettes and cleaners stayed home and cooked the Sunday lunch. The air was charged with pent-up emotion and acrid cigarette smoke. The din entirely indescribable. Many of the projectionists were partially deaf, so the shouting and bawling that went on (natural under such circumstances) made the gathering sound a lot wilder than it really was.

Cinema workers found themselves slipping further and further behind those in other industries. So the hope of bettering their lot by joining a trade union became more widespread. I joined the local branch of NATKE (National Association of Theatrical and Kinematograph employees) soon after starting work at the Embassy. I was not at all keen on joining a union, but Stanley and the others were members ... so I joined too. The only noticeable difference it made to my way of life, was that I had to pay out a shilling a week, receiving in return a little pink membership card.

By now things were beginning to change. Negotiations with the cinema owners, for more pay and better conditions, had dragged on for a year or more. However, we had now been turned down ... so, what were we going to do about it? I hated the thought of going on strike; but, given that there was a great deal of militancy around in those days, I probably would have had little choice.

Our meeting finally broke up at noon, with the resolution to go on strike, if our demands were not met.

In hindsight, it was all rather pathetic. For over twenty years projectionists had received a raw deal: choked by carbon fumes, deafened by un-silenced machinery and working long, anti-social hours for meagre pay. At the height of the cinema boom, when owners were prosperous and could well have afforded to pay more to their staff, we allowed them to get away with it. Now at last the workers had woken up to the possibilities of organised labour. But it was just too late. The collapse of a major part of the cinema industry lay just around the corner. The first chill breaths of impending doom, already beginning to ruffle the brows of the cinema company magnates - the boom was over. The golden years of the cinema beginning to trail behind us.

But, ignorance is bliss. When we met up back at the Embassy that afternoon, we were in a high old state of excitement. To my surprise the most militant among us was our chief, Stanley Briggs.

"What if old Mr. O'Brian takes over running the box when we go out on strike? He used to be a projectionist himself." said Bill Swift.

"He won't have much bloody luck!" growled Stan fiercely. "He'll find both the Maltese crosses broken - quite by accident of course!"

The Maltese cross was the precision-built heart of each projector. Without it films could not be run and the cinema would have to close. Impressed by Stan's extreme attitude, for some weeks afterwards we talked of little else but strikes and negotiations.

Gradually however, the militancy began to leak away as an awareness of realities took its place. At length, the cinema owners convinced the union leaders of the great uncertainties now facing the industry. Salary increases all round would only drive our small circuits into bankruptcy, and throwing a lot of staff on the dole. A very small salary increase was offered, reluctantly accepted and it was all over. I suppose, by the mid 1950s, many of the smaller cinema owners might have been wiser to put their cash into a piggy bank.

Instead they ran their little chains of under-capitalised flea-pits for their handful of ever faithful patrons. Whereas a strike might just have been the welcome excuse needed to call it quits and sell up.

The end of all this strife, as far as I was concerned, was a rise of four shillings (twenty pence) per-week; and an awareness that the cinema industry was no longer a haven of security against unemployment (as I had always believed it to be). Times were changing and perhaps it was time to re-think my future career prospects.

While all this excitement was in train in the cinema industry, we had some excitement at home too. It seemed the neighbours were plotting to murder my mother again! They were building a death-ray machine of some kind. Mum, if she put her head against the party wall, could hear clearly their industrious hammering and tinkering. She was convinced 'they' would use it to kill her once it was complete. She took to having screaming fits in the night and I would leap out of bed, my heart thumping with fright. So, back to Deva Mental Hospital she went. It was a pity it happened at the time of the Jewish Passover, a time of family celebration, feasting and song. I watched, concerned, as the ambulance drove her away ...

The house seemed very empty and still. I felt somehow guilty at packing her off to hospital and an odd sense of disquiet. Sssh, was that a scream?

I leapt to my feet ... no, just the rusty bathroom door hinges. I dozed off for a while only to be awoken by a strange thumping noise coming through the party wall. It ceased suddenly and I wondered how the death-ray machine was coming on. Perhaps mum had been right and there really were fiendish monsters plotting murder and mayhem next door.

This would never do. I rooted out an old rucksack, stuffed it full of unleavened bread, an apple, a bag of sultanas and spare pairs of underpants and socks. I left the house hurriedly in the chill March afternoon without any clear idea as to my destination, I just had to get away from the house for a while, that was all.

After a Crosville bus cross-country journey, I found myself in Shrewsbury. The next day, it was bright and sunny and I wandered around the old cathedral town feeling a lot more calm and collected. So, I went home and back to work. Kind-hearted Mrs. Baum, Danny the barber's wife, made me a hot lunch each day while I was on my own. Several weeks of intensive drug therapy, seemingly brought Mum practically back to normal ... again ... and I took the risk of signing her out to come home ... again! It later turned out that she needn't have gone into hospital at all; she could have had the same drug treatment at home. Nowadays, great gaunt prison blocks like Deva Hospital are no more, and jolly good riddance I say!

Once I was fairly confident of Mum's recovery, I was determined to go along with a plan which my pal Brian Coulter had nagged me about for some time ... a weeks' holiday in Paris no less! In those distant times, such a trip seemed a more daring and exciting adventure, than even a month's holiday in the United States or Australia would seem to youngsters in today's much more blase world.

The Newhaven-Dieppe ferry squared it's shoulders, like a boxer about to wade in against a particularly nasty opponent; throwing itself into the thick of a howling gale roaring down from the North sea. The bar emptied rapidly as Brian and I sat, clutching our untasted drinks.

Facing us across the table were Sonia and Betty, chatting away excitedly. They scarcely seemed to notice the great green sea walls rearing up outside; nor the shuddering crash as they came down upon the boat. Sonia (a large, angular redhead of the rugby fullback variety) and Betty (small and rather pretty) were a couple of ladies who worked in the office at Brian's contracting company. That is how we came to know them; it turned out they were going on the same cheap special-offer package to Paris that we were.

"Let's have another drink!" exclaimed Betty, who seemed to carry her liquor astonishingly well.

Crash, lurch, judder ... the ship performed a grave, yet emphatic waltzing movement that had the rest of the bar cleared in an instant. At the time, ships were built without the blessed stabilisers we have today.

Brian, Sonia and I lurched to our feet to join the stampede to the top deck, grabbing at the railings. We huddled there in the biting wind and lashing rain, a dismal wretched group, while the sailors passed cheerfully around us with mops and buckets.
At one moment I peered into the bar, through a misty porthole. Betty was still sitting at her table. She appeared to have been joined by a few hardy male passengers. There was a row of empty bottles in front of her - quite a girl!

"Hey up Phil. I can see land ahead." Announced Brian, his natural cheerfulness quickly reasserting itself. "Just a few hours from now we'll be slap in the middle of gay Paree. WHOOPEE!"

"Whoopee ..." I echoed faintly.

"Not a bad place at all." Said Brian approvingly, as we dumped our suitcases in the droughty foyer of the hotel Brittanique. We found our room. A great, lofty old-fashioned sort of apartment, with windows opening onto a little balcony. One had the best view of the Gare St. Lazare shunting yards in all Paris. There was a little washbasin, which wheezed and gurgled constantly, as if the smoke from the yards outside had given it bronchitis. There was no toilet or bathroom of course; but, a most thoughtful touch, there was what appeared to be a small foot-bath. "Bloody marvelous idea this," said Brian, easing his aching feet in the running water.

"I don't think you're supposed to use it like that," I said with misgivings, "you're supposed to stick some other part of you in it, though I'm not sure which."

"Never mind that," said Brian cheerfully, "this is what I shall use it for, so there!"

I began to unpack while Brian went on a tour of the hotel. Soon he was back bursting with good news.

"Those two birds from my place, you know, Betty and Sonia, well they're staying at this hotel. I've just bumped into them in the corridor, and guess what?"

I shook my head "What?"

"You and I are taking them out to supper tonight. It's all arranged."

I emptied my wallet on the counterpane and did a quick check on my finances.

"Do you realise Brian," I said, "that we have less than twenty-five pounds each to last us through the week. How the heck are we going to last out if we start taking the girls out to swanky restaurants. We'll starve by the end of the week, that's what!" (£25 was the maximum amount any British tourist was allowed to carry when traveling abroad in those days).

"Give over rabbiting Phil," said Brian impatiently. "of course we won't take them anywhere expensive. But as business men say 'you have to speculate to accumulate' and that's just what we'll be doing."

I had no idea what he was talking about, but I went along with Brian, as I always did. The girls were waiting for us downstairs, both smartly-dressed and wearing about a pound and a half of make-up each.

"Where are you taking us to eat?" asked Betty, quite brusquely "Somewhere nice and posh on the Champs Elysees?"

"Of course not my dear girl," said Brian with feigned indignation, "those sorts of places are strictly for the ignorant Yankee tourists. We'll find some genuine little side-street restaurant, where we can sample some real French cuisine at it's best."

We ended up, to the girls' undisguised indignation, in a sort of French version of Joe's snack bar. We each waded through a rubbery omelette and a small heap of greasy chips; the sort of meal that would have been flung out if served in a Liverpool dockers' canteen.

Later, we strolled down the Boulevard Hausmann in the gathering dusk; and by the time we reached the Arc De Triomphe, the girls were just about on speaking terms with us again. It was a wonderful evening: the bright lights, the unfamiliar odour of French coffee, cigar smoke and garlic ... but above all, the ceaseless flow of humanity past our little table where we had stopped for a Pernod. All the world and his mistress seemed to be strolling up and down the Champs Elysees that night. It seemed far busier even than London's West End.

We left Betty and Sonia at the door of our hotel and, the next day, we lost the girls to a pair of well-heeled U.S. Air Force officers, who did a lightning pick-up job while our backs were turned. We viewed the loss with mixed feelings since our allowance was dwindling at an alarming rate.

And so Friday morning came around, our last full day in Paris. We sat in a little garden where nannies wheeled their prams and old men sat dozing in the warm sunshine.

"Pity we couldn't have met up with a couple of nice French birds." sighed Brian. I tended to agree, it didn't seem right somehow. Two single young men, first time in Paris and no feminine interest.

Two stout old ladies plumped their laden shopping bags beside our seat, and Brian hastily made room for them to sit down next to us. They heard us speaking in English ... then ...

"You 'ave enjoyed your stay in Paris?" asked the stouter of the two.

We nodded and told them of our visits to Notre Dame, the Tuileries and Versailles. The stout lady raised her eyebrows ...

"You 'ave not met any nice young French ladies during your visit?" Digging Brian slyly in the ribs as she leered.

"Why, no." said Brian turning red. "We would have liked to of course but things just didn't turn out."

The two ladies glanced briefly at each other. One of them fished out a grubby card from her capacious handbag, handing it to Brian and saying, "Go to ze cafe Pompadour in ze Rue des Cinq Escargots and tell zem Madame Blanche she sent you. You will be very well looked after. Au revoir mes amis."

They rose and waddled away. We glanced furtively at the little calling card.

"'Catch me going to one of those bloody places," said Brian at last.

"Absolutely disgusting." I agreed ...

The cafe Pompadour was a dingy, dimly-lit establishment in a dingy, dimly lit street, on the fringe of Montmartre. We made our way gingerly inside, sat at a vacant table near the bar and ordered a glass of beer each. We had barely raised our glasses to our lips when ...

"You come wiz me cherie?"

Close to my left ear, the husky voice made my hair literally stand on end and my beer went down the wrong way.

"You go Brian," I spluttered. "I haven't finished my beer yet."

"Neither 'ave I." mumbled Brian looking into the far distance.

The request was repeated and in the end I was led like a lamb to the slaughter, out of the cafe and around the corner into a drab tenement building. The apartment was small and neatly furnished; with a divan bed, an easy chair, pink shaded floor lamp and a crucifix on the wall. It also contained a large grim-faced landlady, who held her hand out as we entered.

"You pay me Fr.1000 and then you pay her Fr.200 for the use of the room." whispered the girl.

I turned out my pockets and placed an assortment of coins and small notes on the bed. We all began counting and, when we had finished, we had a little pyramid of coins like a newly-opened piggy bank stacked on the coverlet. The grand total came to Fr 1180.

"You have no more money?" they asked suspiciously.

By way of reply, I turned out the linings of my pockets. The landlady took her Fr.200 and hobbled out slamming the door. The girl decided to make the best of it, as she had lost a good few minutes of valuable time already.

"Well, what happens next?" I asked cheerfully. "I've never done this sort of thing before, you see." The girl was busy doing something by the washbasin in the corner.

"Perhaps it would help if you took off your trousers monsieur?" she said helpfully ...

... Less than fifteen minutes later I rejoined Brian at our table in the cafe Pompedour. Pleased with myself for having got through the ordeal, I was reminded of nothing so much as the time when I had an X-ray for a suspected slipped disc:

"Take your clothes off, lie over there, thats it. One, two, three, bzzzz. Right, put you clothes back on. Next please."

I grinned and raised my beer mug; the froth only slightly lower than when I left.

"Alright then?" Brian asked anxiously.

I nodded, sipping my beer.

After some minutes a rather skinny, and artificial-looking blonde came over and led Brian away. About half an hour later he returned looking crestfallen.

"All right then?" I asked Brian.

"No it bloody well wasn't!" grunted Brian furiously. "I was too nervous and embarrassed to do it, so she made me pay for extra time into the bargain. Bloody swizz it was! I've a good mind to complain to the British Consul ... and if you don't stop falling about laughing like that, I'll tip you into the river, so help me."

The roar of the projector close to my ear; the glare of the arc light; the plumes of white smoke billowing up the chimney; a tinny Western drawl coming from the monitor loudspeaker; the thump and clatter made by Terrence preparing No. 2

projector; the harsh whine of the re-wind machine in the next room ... it was the old familiar scene once again.

I shaded my eyes against the viewing port and, in place of the trashy gangster film barely visible though the cigarette smoke, tried to conjure up visions of the Tuilleries gardens, the tree-lined boulevards, Sacre Coeur, the Mona Lisa ...

"Alright then Phil?" asked Terrence coming round with the cream soda in a paper cup.

"Fine, just fine." I replied, sipping the soda gratefully. It was back to earth again with a bump.

Reel Twenty

This Sunday only:

"The Masked Pirate"

and

"Challenge to Lassie"

"The King is dead. Princess Elizabeth has been told the sad news, while stuck up a fig tree somewhere in the African jungle. She'd climbed up as princess ... she came down as The Queen. The BBC will be closing down for twenty-four hours as a mark of respect."

My home-made bedside radio then crackled into silence. My head ached abominably and I felt a bit feverish. Had I really heard all that strange stuff on the radio, or was it the fever? I wasn't really sure. Sad if the king was dead ... nice old bloke.

Tossing and turning in my darkened bedroom, I had the bloody measles! When I was a kid, all the regular childhood ailments passed me by ... never meeting other kids meant I was most unlikely to catch anything.

Now that I was out in the great big, germ-ridden world, ailments were queuing up to have a go at me. So it was that I took scarlet fever at seventeen-years, measles at twenty-two and chicken pox at fifty-nine!

As I lay there, waiting for the spots to appear, I took time out to have a good old think about where I was going and what, if anything, I hoped to do with my life. I had been at work almost seven years by now, and didn't seem to have very much to show for it ...

Those first few months as a grocers' boy, were merely a mental aberration on the part of the Youth Employment idiot. My career-proper started when I joined the staff of the King's Cinema, as a clueless apprentice. My rapid rise to Chief Op. had been exciting, the work full of interest and there had been plenty of scope for initiative. For example, most films were still in monochrome, so I made up colour wheels to stick in front of the spare projector, adjusting the arc light so as not to burn the plastic. Spinning the wheels gave nice tints of red, blue and green, over the black and white credits (of the feature film on the other machine) ... all in the hope I might make life more interesting for the audience.

An experienced operator would keep an eye on the number of seats occupied. He would adjust the sound balance accordingly, turning up the wick when the hall filled up with over-coated patrons (as they effectively absorbed some of the sound); or during raging gun-shot battles, to make things more realistic or alarming. Indeed, some film producers enlisted the help of the operators in this way. For 'The First Men on Mars' we were asked to put a red filter over the lens, when the spaceship landed, and crank the sound volume flat-out during the rocket take-off.

In the days before Cinerama (let alone Dolby Stereo or surround sound systems) it was up to the skilled projectionist to make things more exciting. I always did my best to do just that.

Once the King's Cinema metamorphosed into the Continental, the films were good too. If not for the lousy pay, and Mr. Clapshaw's caprices, I should probably have never left the place. But here I was at the Embassy, whether or no. The work was easier, responsibility minimal, and the pay not too bad: £5.10p per week ... just about enough to live on. It sure was dull at times though, and the chances of promotion just about nil.

Save that I would slip some ground glass in Stan Briggs's tea mug, I could see no way of climbing any further up the ladder. A year ago such thoughts would have been easily put aside. Now it was niggling away at me to get up, get out and get on with it!

One of these days, I thought, the right girl would show up (despite my previous weird misadventures), with the prospect of marriage, mortgage, children, ..., and so on. It was bad enough having a job which left mum sitting on her own every night, but it seemed somehow worse to inflict that sort of loneliness on one's wife. On reflection the prospect of marriage definitely appealed to me. Mr. Isidore Schloss, the accredited matchmaker (or 'shadchan') of our local Jewish community, had already some words with me on this subject!

"Have you got yourself a nice Yiddish girl yet, Philly? No? Das ist nisht gut. A nice respectable young man from a good Jewish family ... it's time we saw you under the Chuppah. Otherwise, the Lord alone (blessed be he) knows what temptations you might fall into."

Mr. Schloss had waylaid me as I came out of the synagogue after one of my rare visits ...

"Well Philly, tell me, is there someone?" persisted Mr. Schloss.

(I bloody loathed being called "Philly")

"Er, no Mr. Schloss." I admitted.

"Philly, have I got a girl for you?" Mr. Schloss wafted an imaginary kiss in absent tribute to the chaste maiden in question. Taking my arm firmly in his, he marched me along in the wake of the trilby-hatted worshippers on their way home to Sabbath lunch.

Mr. Schloss was a large, heavy-jowled man; kindly and very pious, with an elephantine sense of humour. He would waggle a chubby finger in the air to emphasise his points.

"You're not a rich boy, true; but you're steady and honest, so all the more reason to marry into a comfortable family. Sadie's father is a good, pious man; and has brought up his daughter in the strict orthodox tradition. It would be an excellent match."

"What's Sadie like, Mr. Schloss?" I put in.

He was quite disconcerted, as he said ...

"What in the name of all that's holy have looks got to do with the matter?" Schloss: wagging his finger archly.

"She has a wooden leg, false teeth, a patch on one eye, and she croaks like a frog! What a question! As if I would persuade you to marry an ugly girl, huh?"

Mr. Schloss sensed that I remained less than convinced, and made me promise to go along to Hessy's Music Store on some excuse; when I might see this paragon in person, as she served at the record counter. As a matter of fact, some days later I did go along to Hessy's. I took a quick peep at the girl behind the 78s counter - and promptly fled! Girl? Huh! She must have been at least fifty-five; with warts, buck-teeth and quite a pronounced squint. What did Schloss take me for?

I later learned that it was the manageress I'd spotted. It seemed Sadie had gone off to powder her nose or something. Lucky old Sadie! I believe she subsequently married well, despite Mr. Schloss's machinations!

My aching head eased and, like stars peeping out after an evening storm, my spots began to appear. I examined them critically - not bad ... but itchy, very itchy! On consideration, I could do without Mr. Schloss's help. One day my dream girl would appear, and then, bingo! That would be it. The more I thought about it, the more certain I became that I must leave the cinema industry as soon as possible. Quite apart from the unsociable hours, the bad pay and the lack of prospects, there were disquieting rumours to consider.

Television, it was said, was rapidly becoming a serious threat to the cinema. Certainly, the local cinemas were beginning to lose custom at an alarming rate. The drop in takings did seem to coincide with all those new TV aerials, now mushrooming over roof tops apparently everywhere and quite suddenly.

Some new TV transmitter had set up in business in the area. What was it that Sam McFann, the Westrex man, gloomily prophesied during his last visit? Half of Britain's cinemas would be closed within the next few years, and perhaps not one cinema in five would be left in business by the end of the sixties. It seemed incredible. Yet, if there were any truth to these forebodings, it made more sense than ever to get out, before one were trampled underfoot in the rush of other projectionists looking for work.

We bought our first television set in 1953. A great, clumsy, wooden-box affair, with a single black and white BBC channel, and twelve-inch screen. It was a great boon to mum though. She thankfully settled down in front of it, during the long and lonely evenings when I was at work.

"You needn't bother with the complimentary cinema passes now, Phil ..." she said after a few weeks "... it's much nicer staying here at home by the fire, and watching the television, than going out to the pictures in all the cold and wet."

A lot of other people's mums and dads evidently felt the same way ... the first cinemas, the oldest and shakiest ... they closed their doors ...

So it was that I began job hunting again in earnest. By now I had a smattering of electrical theory and, thanks to the work I did for my friend Danny Baum the barber, I was fairly adept at the practical side of repairing radios. I was by now reasonably articulate, and my slightly rough ride through the school of life had rid me of much excess naivety. Even though my schooling, in a more academic sense, was still quite inadequate.

One might have imagined it not too difficult to find a suitable job in the electrical industry, where the hours were less than sixty per-week, and the pay more than £5.10p. However, I was in for a rude awakening ...

The Personnel Manager at Rushworth and Dreaper electrical store rustled some papers while taking notes. The interview had gone very well so far. I had answered the technical questionnaire without any difficulty; and my total lack of academic attainment, had not even been mentioned. It seemed I might be all set to start a new career as a radio repair engineer, at one of Liverpool's largest and best known radio and TV firms ...

Suddenly the man stiffened and peered closely at an item in my completed application form. He rose from his desk in agitation and pointed an accusing finger at me. "You ... w'work in the ... s's'cinema?" he stuttered in disbelief.

"Yes it says so there, what of it?" I asked out of curiosity.

"I just don't believe it," said the interviewer, reddening with indignation, "you come to one of Liverpool's most respected, and reputable stores ... you a projectionist ... and actually expect us to take you on. Incredible!"

"What's incredible about it?" I asked, rapidly overwhelmed by a sense of my irritation.

He handed back my papers and said severely:

"It is, I believe, generally accepted that cinema employees are among the idlest bunch of layabouts in the working population. Your trade is riddled with drunks and petty criminals of every description. You yourself may well be a solitary exception, but I have no intention of taking the risk. Good day to you Mr. Rosen."

There was nothing to say. I took up my birth certificate, cloth cap and left.

I tried other firms; firms of less self-advertised respectability. Nonetheless, the response was invariably the same: "Projectionist? Sorry son! Don't think you'll really suit us" was the standard brush-off. It seemed I was virtually unemployable outside anything but the cinema industry itself.

I half thought of putting 'professional pickpocket' as my present job, on the next application form I completed, to see if the response was any more favourable. However, pursuing my twenty-third job application, I took the old No. 40 bone-shaker tram. It growled up Brownlow Hill to the Automatic Telephone and Electric Works in Edge Lane. By now I was quite hardened to it all with a growing sense of apathy. My chance of success seemed so remote as to scarcely merit the four-pence tram fare. Still, it was a nice sunny day and somewhere a bit different to go on one's day off.

The tram ground to a halt outside the works, and subsequently I entered the seemingly enormous factory building. It was the first very large factory I had ever seen, and I found it quite impressive: acres of workshops; the hum and rattle of machinery; the deft, flickering fingers of hundreds of women as they sat in long, neat rows, absorbed in their intricate tasks. I later learned that over twelve-thousand people worked at this site alone.

All this was purposeful bustle, as scores of people hurried to-and-fro about their appointed tasks. The contrast between this busy scene, and that of the monastic seclusion of the operating box, struck me most forcibly.

The Electronics Department was much quieter and more decorous. Serious-faced men in white coats, pottered gravely among a wilderness of electronic equipment; adjusting dials, peering at circuit diagrams, examining closely the little jiggling, green traces on oscilloscope screens. It all seemed tremendously technical and almost overwhelmingly exciting.
I was interviewed by a foreman inspector called Frank. He was a chubby little man in a white coat, who sat in a small office with waist-high partitioning. While we talked, he kept

a wary eye on his allotted portion of the assembly lines just outside. To the left, and right down the long hall, his colleagues kept an eye on their own sections; rather like signalmen along a busy stretch of railway line.

The hall was well lit, clean and more like an oversized laboratory than a factory floor. Only the faint pipping noise of oscillators, and the occasional subdued rattle of a soldering iron being replaced in its holder, made tentative intrusions on the overall air of veritably pastoral tranquility. It was difficult to appreciate the fact that, while we sat there, millions of pounds worth of complex electronic equipment was being assembled and tested for shipment to places all over the world.

"Describe that circuit, please." said Frank, pushing a simple diagram in front of me ...

"What would happen if we increased the value of that resistor? If we opened that switch would the power increase or decrease? Would that capacitor be insulated with wax paper or with mica ..." and so on ...

I answered each question without difficulty.

He glanced down my application form ... I held my breath.

"Hmm. It says here ... you are a projectionist. Must be an interesting job. I'm quite fond of Westerns myself."

Frank smiled and put away his papers.

"Right, Philip," he said, rising "that's all okay then. Call at the Employment Office on your way out, to see about your insurance cards and so on."

My jaw dropped!

"Y'you mean I've g'got th'the job?" I gasped.

"Certainly," said Frank "see you on Monday week then ... yes Jack, what's the trouble? Oscillator acting up again, eh? Be with you in minute ..."

Frank hurried away to deal with this new problem, while I wandered out in a daze, quite unable to believe in my good luck.

A few days later, a letter plopped onto the door mat confirming my appointment as an Electrical Testing Engineer, on a starting salary of £7.10s (seven pounds and ten shillings, or £7.50) per week.

Hours: Monday-to-Friday, 8 am to 5.45 pm ... annual pay review ... promotion to staff status with company pension after probationary period ... report to Personnel Department on arrival.

It was probably the single, most important letter I ever received in my life ...

Taking mum out to celebrate my success, we sat in state in the best seats in the Capitol Cinema. We laughed ourselves silly at the antics of Danny Kaye in his latest comedy film. When the house lights went up for the interval, and the choc-ice girls lept into action, I craned my neck to look up at the tiny shadows moving to-and-fro behind the operating box viewing ports. Already feeling a sense of remoteness, I was no longer an operator on his day off. I was just a member of the cinema-going public, like anyone else. I visualised the operators imprisoned up there, with the never-ceasing roar of the projectors. Had I really been cooped up behind tiny windows like those for over six years? Already this seemed utterly incredible to me.

The next day, I handed in my notice and Mr. O'Brian shook hands gravely, wishing me well in my newly-chosen career.

Stanley Briggs said, "You're bloody daft you are going to work in a factory. Nasty noisy places; crowds of people everywhere. I can't understand why anyone would want to give up operating. Nice, quiet respectable job operating is. You could have been a Chief at one of the big city cinemas if you'd just bided your time and had a bit of patience. You're all the same you young fellers - restless and impatient, like a duck with feathers up its arse."

Seeing that he wasn't getting anywhere with his attempt to impart grave wisdom, Stanley sloped off to the Pub for some liquid refreshment. No doubt he wanted to reconcile himself to the loss of one of his least eccentric projectionists.

That afternoon he arrived back bearing a saucepan-shaped parcel, done up in very faded brown paper. He advanced towards me, his face oddly twisted and deformed. I realised with a start that he was actually attempting a friendly smile.

"Here you are then Phil. A little keepsake from old Stan." he said, handing me the parcel. "It kept me off the streets and out of mischief when I was a lad. I hope it'll do as much for you too."

Good grief, it was Stan's old banjo!

And so, here I stand; for the very last time, by Number One projector, watching the last few feet of the second house feature film run through the machine. I open the film magazine door and estimate the remaining film with a practiced eye.

I call: "God save the King, I mean God save the Queen coming up!"

Terrence takes up his stance by the tabs switch and the house lights; Bill Swift poised at the non-sync; Stanley in the rewind room checking off the film packing cases, ready for the transport men in the morning ...

Gregory Peck and Audrey Hepburn enter into their big clinch ...

"Right, that's it. 'The End' Some nice romantic, pink tab lights please ..."

God save the queen plays, as our patrons shuffle to release themselves too from the sleazy pit.

Close the tabs ... bring up the house lights ... fade in the non-sync (nothing like the Radetzky March for clearing the patrons out fast) ... douse the arc and shut down the projector ...

And that's it. The end of Phil Rosen's celebrated career in show business ...

"What's this fellers? Aah, hey, you shouldn't have ..."

Crisps, custard pies, sticky buns and two bottles of Cream Soda.

"... well that's just super. Come on Stanley, come join the fun. Have some Cream Soda just the once, it won't kill you. What d'you mean 'It bloody well will.' Well that's not very friendly is it ... is it now!"

Epilogue

Today, not one of the thirteen cinemas, which were around in my home town of Wallasey back in the 1950s, still exists as such. They all closed down between 1957 and the early 1980s. So I got out just in time!

Three of them did, however, undergo the metamorphosis into cut-price supermarkets; where mouse droppings are certainly not sieved out of the lentils and pearl barley by pimply-faced apprentices (I understand that this is all done automatically these days).

My old Cinema, the Continental, was demolished some years after closing in 1963.

The Embassy, the second cinema at which I worked, closed its doors in 1959; later struggling as a somewhat sleazy night club.

Although the Winter Gardens cinema closed, much like the rest, its mighty Wurlitzer organ was saved. It found a loving home in the small 'semi' of a neighbour - a true devotee of the cinema-related organ. The console took up most of his living room! The remaining 'works' were disposed in various parts of the house and garage. The organ's preserver was a competent performer himself, taking considerable delight in giving recitals to his friends (and indeed anyone else who happened to have their windows open, within a radius of a mile or so downwind).

Sadly, I lost track of many of my old colleagues. But I did manage to follow the fortunes of some for a while:

Wally Tate, the philandering operator at the Continental, went on to become a car salesman. I don't think he ever married because, as he used to say, "After all my experiences with married women, old son, I'd never feel able to trust one of my own!"

Manager at the Continental, Harold Clapshaw (and his pretty wife Julia) fought a gallant rearguard action against the advancing tide of cinema closures.
They moved on from one cinema to the next until there were none left to treasure. The last I heard, they had set up a little sweets and tobacco retail business.

Casting around for pastures new, Cinema owner Hyman Bloom and his faithful Gimble, settled on stationary pictures instead of the moving variety, going on to trade in the fine arts business.

My old Chief Stanley Briggs took early retirement.

Our doorman, old Joe Crampton, reluctantly also took early retirement on his 80th birthday.

Terrence, my co-worker at The Embassy, went to work in a chocolate factory. Although the going was sticky at times, there was always plenty of spare goodies for his young friends and relatives.

I last spotted Mr. O'Brian, sometime supervising manager of the North Western cinema circuit, hunched up behind the passenger seat of a car with 'L' plates. He was attempting to pass round Liscard roundabout <u>against</u> the flow of traffic. Mr. O'Brian was the driving instructor!

My pal Brian Coulter married and worked for a time as an electrician. Then a long spell of bad luck ... he was badly burned, partly through his own carelessness. Taking bad advice he sued the firm he worked for and lost his case. Worse, he found that word got around, and nobody would employ him thereafter. A salutary warning against calling in the legal profession in these cases.

Unfortunately, I lost track of our scatter-brained junior Alfie Beaton, and so cannot be sure if he ever did achieve his stated ambition to become a brain surgeon.

Of course, in more recent years, there has been a resurgence of the cinema. Multiscreen cinemas, offering up to ten or more different shows, have sprung up in the suburbs where parking is easier. The few cinema projectionists who remain today are solitary creatures indeed.

Often a single operator is sufficient to run a whole evening's programme. A central operating box has several machines beaming down into the different auditoria; all of which are operated automatically. The projector is loaded with its several miles of film at the start of the programme. Clean halogen lamps replace the old smoking arc lamps.

The film snakes from its massive reel, several feet in diameter, all around the room. Running through the projector itself, it then runs back onto the reel again ready for the next showing. Timers are set to operate the lights, tabs and music at appropriate places in the programme. The operator presses the starting button ... and that's that! Even the rewinding is done automatically. The operator needs still to have a good deal of technical knowledge, in the event that things do go wrong; but most of the art and showmanship of the job has gone.

At the time of writing (2011), even this high degree of mechanisation is seemingly, naturally obsolete. Digital projection is becoming mainstream. Huge rolls of film are being replaced by a tiny silicone chip, bearing a whole evening's programme! The chip is popped into a specialised computer and a digital projector does the rest.

Given the high degree of familiarity of today's youngsters with computer technology, it could almost be that the team of specialised projectionists, needed to run a show back in the 'Fifties, could be replaced by a single gum-chewing teenager!

For those in the audience who appreciate a happy ending, I am happy to be able to supply one ...

Not long after leaving the cinema business, and starting work as an electrical engineer, I met and later married the best girl in the world. Then, children and grandchildren, all to be hugely proud of.

I am just about getting used to married life by now, and about to celebrate our 55th wedding anniversary ;-)

With my wife Sheila's help and encouragement, I studied hard four evenings-a-week at college for several years. I attained a Higher National Diploma in Engineering and was able to write M.I.R.E and C.Eng. after my name.

Ultimately, I became a senior engineering manager running a department staffed by University graduates. Useful since my maths never quite came up to scratch, but now it didn't seem to matter so much. With some satisfaction, I was able to say:

"Good heavens Fothergill, fancy bothering me with a simple mathematical problem like that. Now do go away like a good chap and work it out for yourself."

One of my most proud moments was being elected President of an international technical committee, and having folk stand to attention as 'M. le President' entered the hall.

My keen interest in all things electrical has stayed with me. I have written many technical papers, taken out several patents and travelled the world - visiting over thirty countries, giving lectures and attending conferences on my pet subject: the protection of electrical systems.

On retiring from my full-time career, I took to running extra-curricular evening courses in technology history, for undergraduate students at our local University. I had never managed to get to University myself, so I sometimes feel a sense of irony when setting and marking papers for these young hopefuls (some of whom regarded me as more an ivory-towered professor, than an ex-grocer's boy and factory-hand).

I have kept my interest in the cinema; and even now, whenever we go to see movie, I pop into the operating box for a chat with the bored and solitary operator. I try to impart to them what life was like in the 'box' sixty-or-more years ago (which is always a hoot).

Finally, I must admit that my post-projectionist career has not been an uninterrupted success story. I never was able to come to grips with Stanley's banjo; getting only as far as 'Way down upon the Swanee river (plink, plink) far, far away, ...' Our neighbours rightly soon put an end to that anyway.

Glossary of Terms

Technical, Local Dialect and Yiddish

Chuppah ('Chooppar'): The marriage canopy at a Jewish wedding.

Holophane: The trade name for specialised equipment once used to project a sequence of coloured light onto tabs or screen.

Jigger ('Jiggeh'): Liverpudlian term for narrow alleyway.

Judy ('Joodie'): Liverpudlian term for young lady.

Meshuggah ('Meshoogar'): Yiddish term for crazy or eccentric.

Non-sync ('Non-sink'): Record Player used for playing background music during intervals, etc. (derivation: non-synchronised turntable not connected to the projector itself).

"**Nu?**": Almost untranslatable Jewish greeting. Nearest meaning: "Well, what's new?"

Operating Box: The projection suite where the projectors and associated equipment for running the film show are housed.

Operator: Projectionist or person in charge of making up film programmes, running the projector and operating all electrical equipment in the cinema. Typical staff: Chief Op, Second Op, Third Op. or Junior.

Projection Mechanism: The heart of the projector containing the lens and drives for moving the film through, as well as the sound head. Also known as 'machine'.

Purim: A time when Jewish children dress-up and re-enact the biblical story of good Queen Esther, and the wicked King's minister Haman, at the court of weak-kneed King Ahasuerus.

Ration Book: A book of crude tokens issued to the public during WWII. Folk would redeem their ration vouchers against staple food stuffs and other provisions; such as soap and such. This means of nation-wide, collaborative economy continuing until 1954.

Rewind Room: Workroom adjacent to the operating box where film is made up into programmes, stored, rewound after each showing and repaired as necessary.

Shadchan: ('Shadshan'): Marriage broker. One who arranges marriages between suitable Jewish families.

Synagogue: A synagogue is a Jewish place of worship. Also spelled 'synagog', it is derived from the Greek 'synagoge', meaning: "assembly" or "house of assembly." More specifically "a house of prayer."

Tabs: The curtains across the cinema screen (from the French Tableau).

Teddy Boy: 1950s equivalent of today's excitable teenager; notably a fan of Rock and Roll music.

"**The Dole**": State unemployment benefit.

"**Schlemiel**" ('Shlemeel') Yiddish term meaning Idiot.

Illustrations

Sources

Leicester museums.
'The Complete Projectionist'.
'The Silver screens of Wirral' (history of Wallasey cinemas).
Wallasey News newspaper.
Wallasey reference library.
Wirral archives office.

Wallasey News

Wednesday, 12 April, 2000

The Voice of Wirral for 120 Years

WIRRAL NEWS GROUP: Birkenhead News, Wallasey News, Bromborough and Bebington News, Hoylake and West Kirby News

EMPLOYMENT/ *Jobs to go as credits roll on old picture house*

CLOSURE IS SAD ENDING FOR CINEMA

THE last cinema in Wallasey is to close with the loss of 28 jobs.

Above:

The mid-1950s saw mass closure of cinema across the country, as people stayed at home to watch programmes on the new-fangled television set, instead of paying their weekly visit to the flicks. Time for the projectionist to seek pastures new ... which I duly did.

In this Wallasey News feature (year 2000), I am photographed with an old projector of the time.

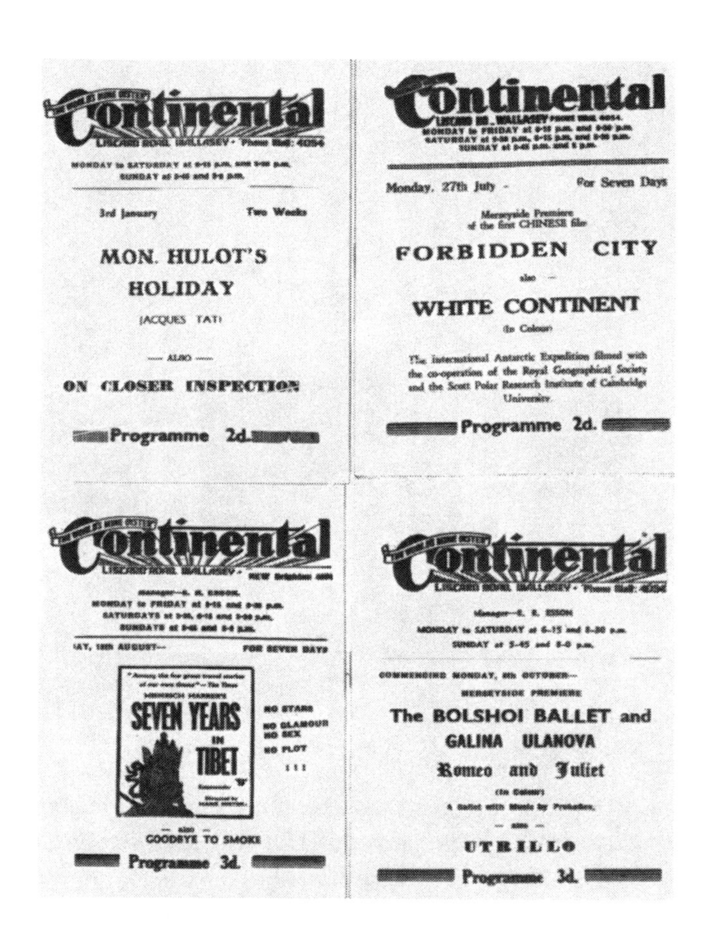

Above:

The first continental films advertised on Merseyside; where the tatty old Kings' Picture House transformed into the up-market Continental Cinema. Here we showed French, Italian and Russian films, as well as opera and ballet. Quite and education for us projectionists!

"Pasez moi le spool nombre trous sil vous plait ... old bean!"

Above:
Danny's Barber Shop was next to the Embassy cinema, where projectionists went for their 'crew cut' hair styles, Brylcream and possibly '... something for the weekend.'
Repairing Danny's old radio sets gave this customer vital experience for his latter career in electronic engineering.

Above:
The old Liscard Palace cinema was a 'pre-historic' relic in the shopping centre of town. It was a throw-back to the art-nouveau, fussy ornamentation of Edwardian times. In later years a bleak modern frontage appeared and the building metamorphosed into a Tesco supermarket.

LITTLE CINEMA — FIRST FOR ENTERTAINMENT.

SUNDAY, OCT. 17th.—Randolph SCOTT—Ann RICHARDS in BADMAN'S TERRITORY. (U). (Continuous from 5-0).

MONDAY, OCTOBER 18th —— FOR TWO DAYS.
CHESTER MORRIS
MARGOT GRAHAME in **COUNTERFEIT.** (A) (3-11 6-58—9-20)
Also Denis WEBB in THE FLAMINGO AFFAIR. (A). (2-15—6-00—8-14).

WEDNESDAY, OCTOBER 20th —— FOR TWO DAYS. BY PUBLIC DEMAND.
ANTON WALBROOK—
SALLY GRAY in **DANGEROUS MOONLIGHT.** (U)
(2-48—6-43—8-50).

FRIDAY, OCTOBER 22nd.—— FOR TWO DAYS.
BORIS KARLOFF—
ROGER PRYOR in **The Man They Could Not Hang.** (H)
(3-16—7-01—9-16).
Also Jack La RUE in BUSH PILOT. (U). (2-15—6-00—8-11).
(No children under 16 can be admitted).

Above:
An Advert of the time, for the weekly cinema programme at the Liscard Road Picture House. This would have appeared in the Wallasey News.

The Kings Picture House was where I spent much of my early cinema life projecting films for the local 'picture' goers. This cinema typically showed no less than eight films per-week, based on the principle that "if you can't afford to show good new films, then show as many rubbish ones as possible instead.

Above: Mrs. Sheila Rosen and I back in 1957. Newly-weds at the time, this picture was taken shortly after my leaving the cinema profession for a decent daytime job in electrical engineering.

Above: My proud father at his tailors' shop, The Liverpool & District Tailoring Company.

Above: A 1940s cinema projector. Seven-foot-tall, this monster weighed half a tonne. Today, such monsters have been replaced by much more automatic means of projection; and are, in fact, in the process of being entirely superseded by digital projectors, fed by tiny silicon chips bearing a whole evening's performance!

Queens Picture House (1948)

Above: The Queens Picture House was another relic of the cinematographic stone-age. The Queens' and the Kings' cinema, where I worked, shared the same newsreel. So, I was forced to wear a groove in the pavement each night while carrying the wretched spool of film across town from one cinema to the other and back again.

Above: My family, at the time of writing this book. From back-to-front, left-to-right:
Our son Alex Rosen, Alex and Sue's daughter and son, Natalie and Daniel, daughter in-law Sue Rosen and Karl Littardi, our son in-law.
Sheila Rosen, my wife, and me Phil C. Rosen, with our daughter Judith Littardi holding son Massimo.

Other titles from P.C. Rosen include

- ★ Three Pfennings for a Waltz
- ★ A New Beginning
- ★ Lenny
- ★ Mr. Dodgson Through the Looking Glass
- ★ The Night Watchman's Tale
- ★ The Birthday Ghosts
- ★ A Beastly Business
- ★ The Great Town Clock at Amstelwyjk
- ★ Henry
- ★ Interval Talk